In It For The Money
Superg...

Exclusive Distributors

International Music Publications Limited
Southend Road, Woodford Green, Essex IG8 8HN, England

International Music Publications Limited
25 Rue D'Hauteville, 75010 Paris, France

International Music Publications GmbH, Germany
Marstallstraße 8, D-80539 Munchen, Germany

Nuova Carish S.R.L.
Via M.F. Quintiliano 40, 20138 Milano, Italy

Danmusik
Vognmagergade 7, DK-1120 Copenhagen K, Denmark

Warner/Chappell Music Australia Pty Ltd.
3 Talavera Road, North Ryde, New South Wales 2113, Australia

Folio © 1997 International Music Publications Ltd
Southend Road, Woodford Green, Essex IG8 8HN

Music Transcribed by Barnes Music Engraving Ltd., East Sussex TN22 4HA
Printed by The Panda Group · Haverhill · Suffolk CB9 8PR · UK
Binding by ABS · Cambridge

Photograph pages Kevin Westenberg, Cover Photo; James Fry, Cover Design; The Designers Republic

Hello,

*and welcome to this, the second Supergrass song book.
Thanks for lining our pockets once again but be aware!
These songs are notated by some boffin and may vary from
the very loose knowledge of formal music notation used by
Supergrass. This may create the impression that we employ
these ten fret, arthritically challenged muso chords when
performing, but nothing could be further from the truth.
So, please use this book as a guide and not as gospel. At
least you can rip off some of the more interesting chords to
impress your mates.*

Still, enough of my yakking, Enjoy!

SOMETIMES I MAKE YOU SAD.

Shut out the world you can do it
Then let me climb inside
There's only one way you can do it
Just let your mind unwind
So to the world I say hello
But the people don't care
Cause there's nothing out there

Once there was a boy
Spent days all alone
In a rowing boat
Living in Rome
Set sail for the sea
But get back on this song

Young love we'll have to get through it
Sometimes I make you sad
Stamp out the beat so you can do it
it's like the world we share
And when the curtain falls on you
The people don't care
Cause there's nothing out there

Shut out the world you can do it
Then let me climb inside
There's only one way you can do it
Just let your mind unwind
So to the world I say hello
But the people don't care
Cause there's nothing out there

TONIGHT.

Going to a party and you'll never want to leave it tonight
You'll wanna see the band playing bish bash bosh tonight
I know it's just a feeling but I know I'm gonna see her tonight
And everybody knows they're never gonna sleep tonight

She said when, I said why, Tonight

Going to a party and you'll never want to leave it tonight
You'll wanna see the band playing bish bash bosh tonight
I know it's just a feeling but I know I'm gonna see her tonight
And everybody knows they're never gonna sleep tonight

She said when, I said why, Tonight, I went dry, Yeah, Tonight

And a gun in his hand
And he's looking at mine
And he's 2 foot 2
But you don't know where I am
When you see what I've ben through
And he's phoning his cab
When he's seemingly fine
But he's seen me too
But you don't know what you are
When you see what I've been through

She said when, I said why, Tonight,

She said when, I said why, Tonight, I went dry, Yeah, tonight

GOING OUT.

If you want to go out
If you want to go out
Read it in the papers
Tell me what it's all about, Yeah

If you want to stay home
If you want to stay home
Freedom of the papers
All you ever need to know
Freedom of the papers
All you've got to do...
Oh no, oh no

If you want to play home
If you want to play home
Freedom from the papers
All you've got to do...
Oh no, Oh no

If you want to go out
If you want to go out
Read it in the papers
Tell me what it's all about
Read it in the papers
All you've got to do..
Oh no, not me

If you want to go out (repeated)

LATE IN THE DAY.

It's late in the day
I'm thinking of you
Things that you say
So long, so long for me

It's late in the day
I'm talking to you
Hear what I say
So long, so long for me

All the time I've thought of you
In an ordinary way
We'd slip off down the oily way
And all I really have to say
Is people pass along the way
Had thoughts of you and me again

I lay on my bed
Searching my mind
Lighten my load
So long, so long for me

I sleep on the road
Dream of a sound
Coming my way
So long, so long for me.

Chorus

All the time I've thought of you
In an ordinary way
We'd slip off down the oily way
And all I really have to say
As people pass along the way
I close my eyes and turn away
All the time I've been with you
In an ordinary day
We'd trip off down the oily way
All I really have to say
Is people pass along the way
And thoughts of you and me again

SUN HITS THE SKY.

I know a place where the sun hits the sky
Everything changes and blows out the night
Everyone knows why my tongue can't be tied
'Cos I want to live where the sun meets the sky

I am a doctor, I'll be your doctor
I'm on my way, you won't come down today
Live for the right things, be with the right ones
Or they'll hold you down, they'll turn your world around

Well, I just down't know why the sun hits the sky
Everyone changed as they turned out the light
Living is easy with time on my side
'Cos I want to live where the sun hits the sky

Chorus
Chorus

IT'S NOT ME.

Over their heads I find a place to crawl away
So many times I hear the things we used to say

Into the night the conversation fades away
Losing the drift of all the things I had to say

It's not me, no no not me
But I don't know what is
I try and find my peace of mind
But I know what I miss

Now it's gone (x 3)

As everyone listened
My head turned away
I know what I'm missing
I've nothing to say

Chorus (x2)

RICHARD III.

Got up today, what a day, thanks a million
Spent too much time wondering why I've got an opiniion

I know you want to try and get away
But it's the hardest thing you'll ever know

Waiting in line, terrible time, over familiar
Take them away, they've nothing to say, they're over the hill, yeah

Chorus

Trying to get at you (x 2)
Trying to get at you (x 4)

Chorus (x 2)

G-SONG.

As I walk into the night
I don't feel that my feet have touched the ground
And I want to carry on
But I can't see anyone taking time

There may be troubles in your mind
Maybe tomorrow could be find

I feel like going home
But I don't know if I'm up or coming down
And I feel there's something wrong
But I know it's just the time it takes to climb

Chorus
Repeat Chorus

CHEAPSKATE.

Lift me up and move in closer
Holding on to what I know
She's the one who plays with fire
I see a side you'll never know

I need someone to be around
Cause I'm breaking into life
Somebody stop me
Cause I'm looking for my,
Looking for my high

She's the one who plays with fire
I see a side you'll never know

Chorus

Chorus
You and me YEAH!
Now I'm breaking through the door
Somebody stop me
Cause I'm looking for my,
Looking for my high

IN IT FOR THE MONEY.

Here I see a time
To go and leave it all behind
And you know it's wrong to fall

We're in it for the money (repeated)

Got my mind made up
I got my finger on the buton
Going way home
Got the sun turned down
Got a feeling in my pocket
Going way home

And all I can see is all this
And all I can be is you (x 2)

Chorus repeated

HOLLOW LITTLE REIGN.

Uptight thinking things over
Conversations running round my head
Good times last so much longer
Summer lovin' going straight to my head

Some day when I can

Cool skies drinking the sunshine
Feel the wind blowing through my hair
It's our time for talking it over
Take you home fall into my bed

Some day when I can

Sometimes clouds will come over
Leopard spots in front of my eyes
One day when we feel a lot better
Take a train to the coller climbs

Someday when I can

YOU CAN SEE ME.

If you like me, you can buy me and take me home
You can see me on your TV, I'm alone
You can call me, tell your story on the phone
You can hear me over blue seas, I'm alone

You can't see me I'm not really there
You can't see me I'm not really there

When you need me, come and see me and take me out
In the evening, when we're sleepy, lay me down
All the crazies, try and space me, and I don't know
I'm not easy, don't try to please me, Xeonophobe

Chorus

If you like me, you can buy me and take me home
You can see me on your TV, I'm alone
You can call me, tell your story on the phone
You can hear me over blue seas, I'm alone

In It For The Money.

Words and Music by
Daniel Goffey, Gareth Coombes,
Michael Quinn and Robert Coombes

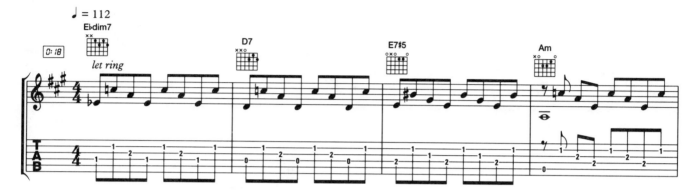

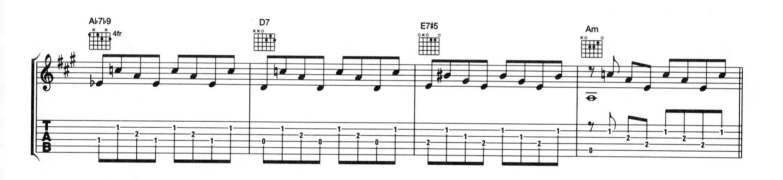

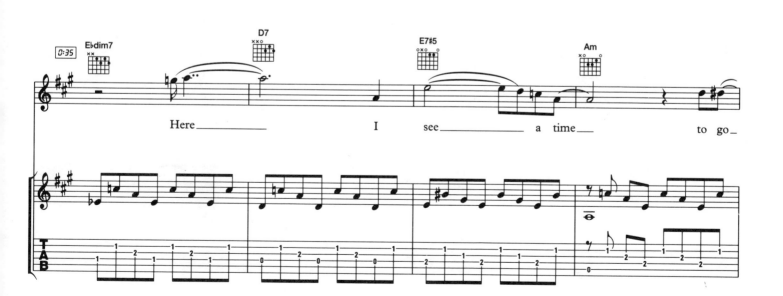

Here_____ I see_____ a time_____ to go_

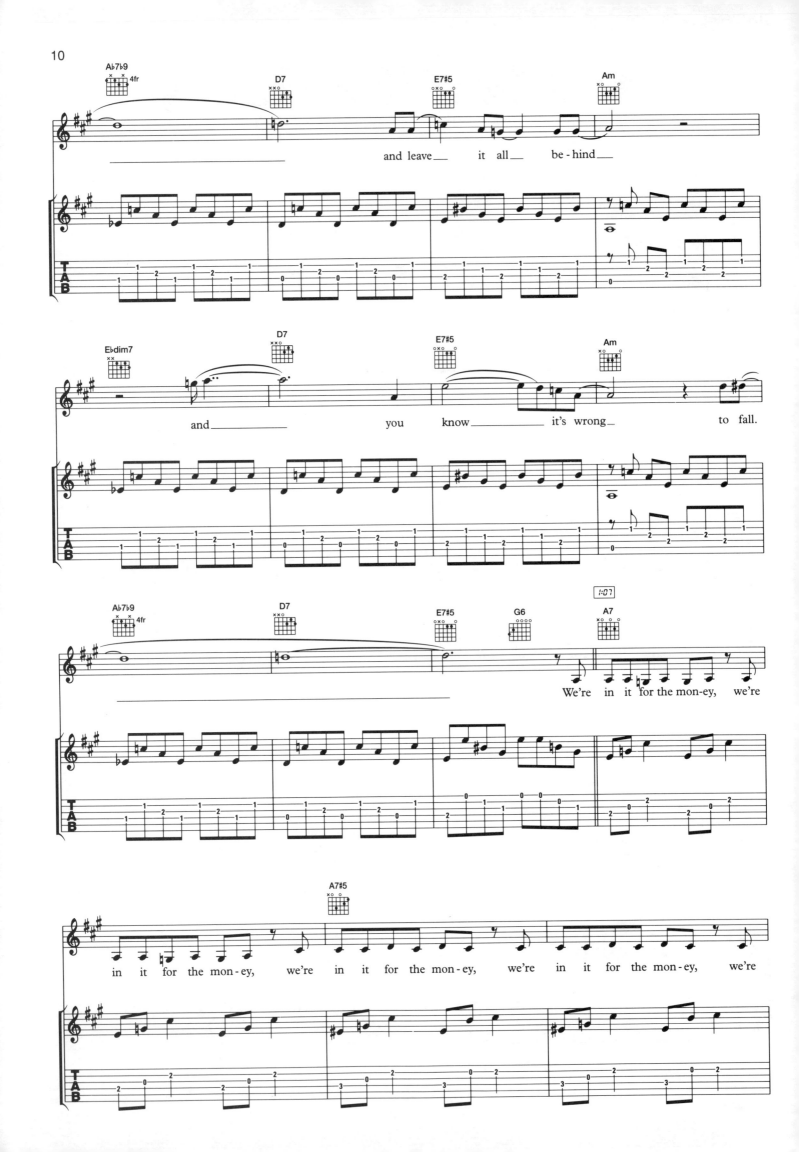

Richard III.

Words and Music by
Daniel Goffey, Gareth Coombes,
Michael Quinn and Robert Coombes

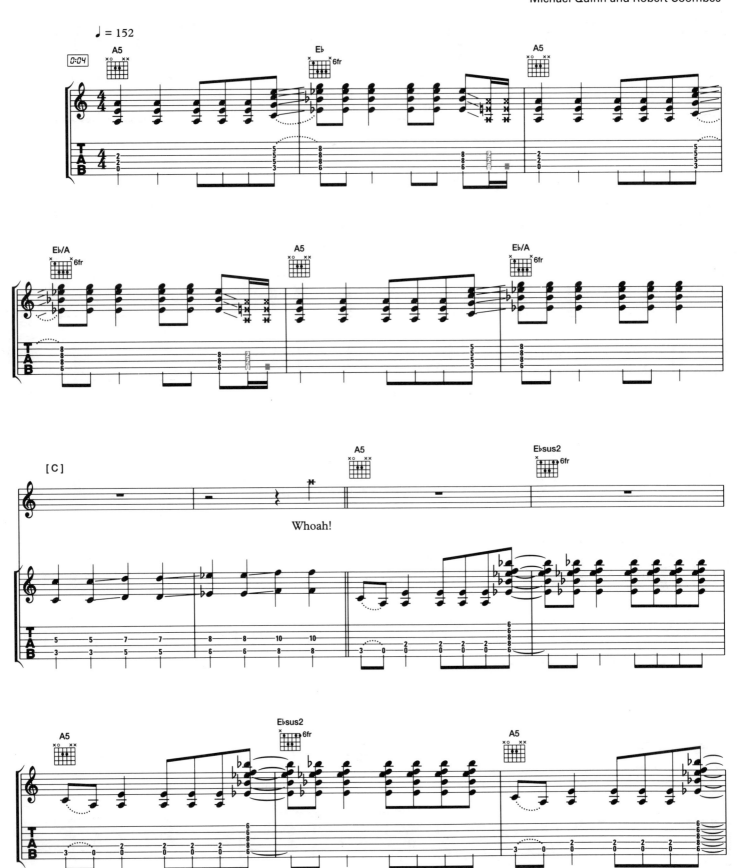

Whoah!

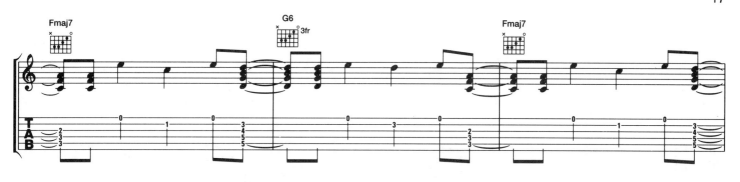

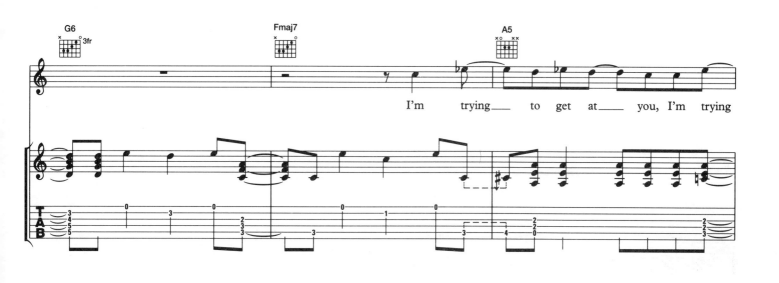

I'm trying___ to get at___ you, I'm trying

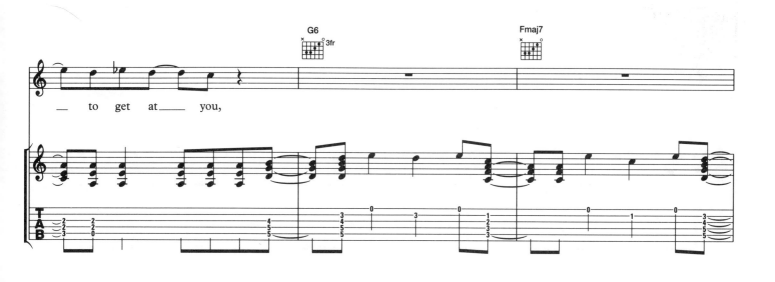

___ to get at___ you,

I'm trying___ to get at___ you, I'm trying___ to get at___ you, I'm trying

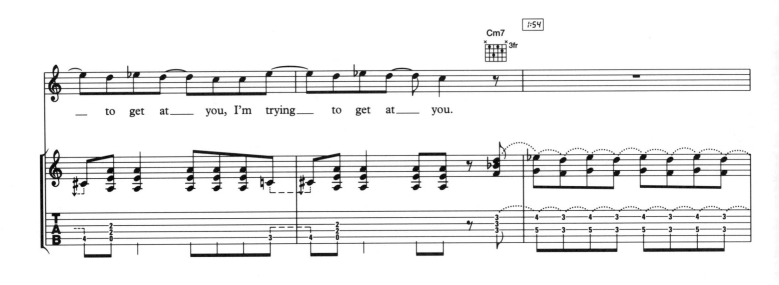

___ to get at___ you, I'm trying___ to get at___ you.

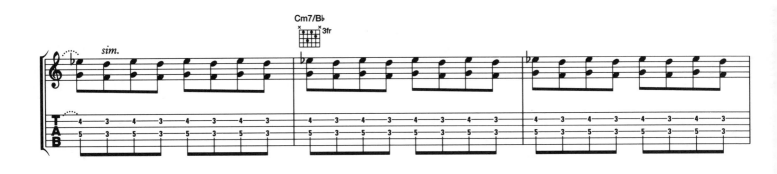

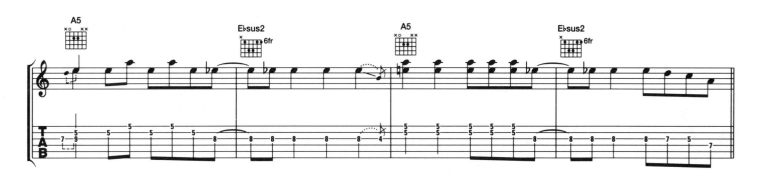

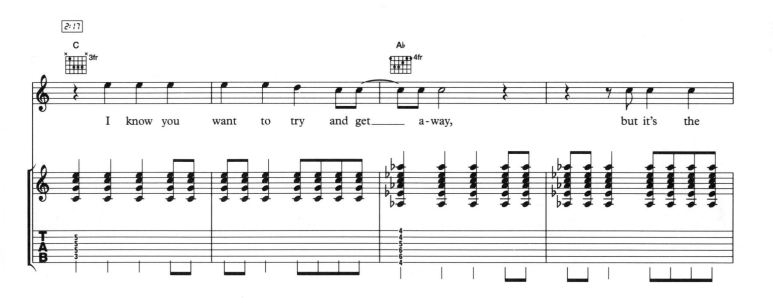

I know you   want   to   try   and   get_____   a - way,   but   it's   the

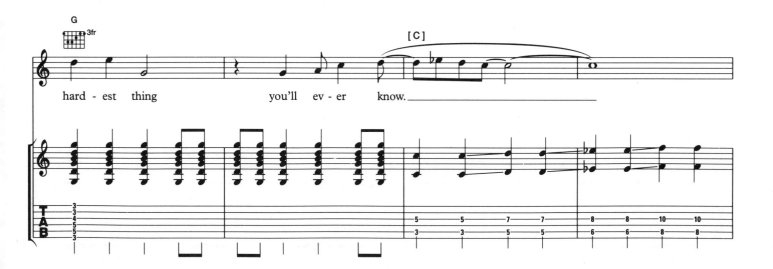

hard - est   thing   you'll   ev - er   know._____

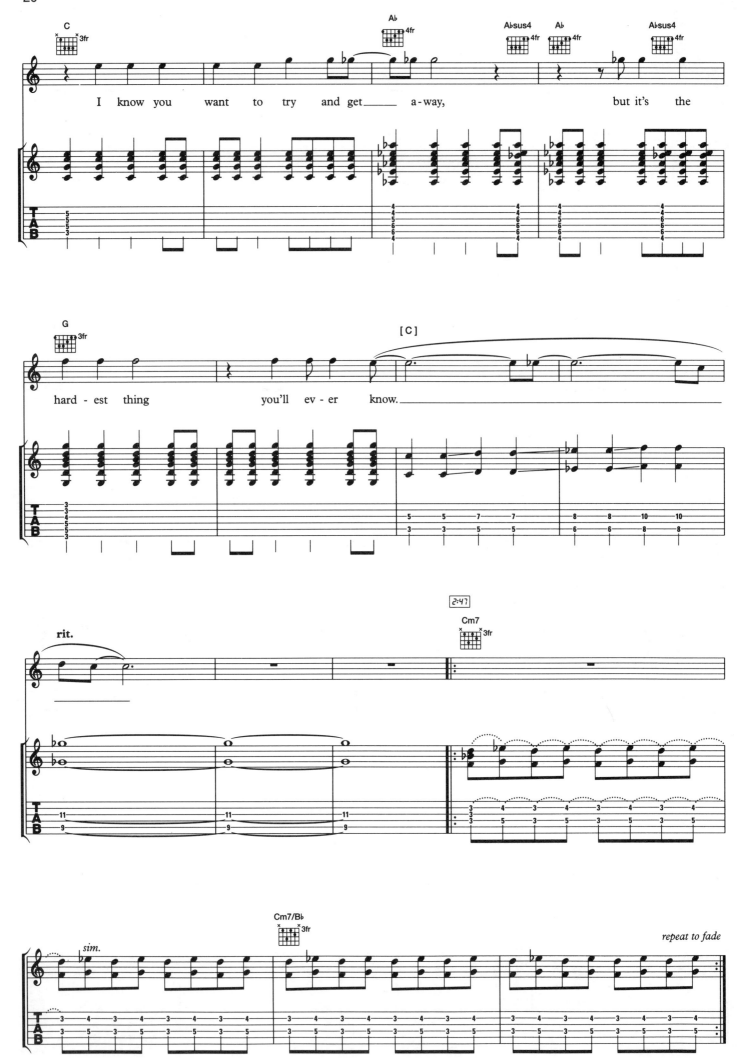

Tonight.

Words and Music by
Daniel Goffey, Gareth Coombes,
Michael Quinn and Robert Coombes

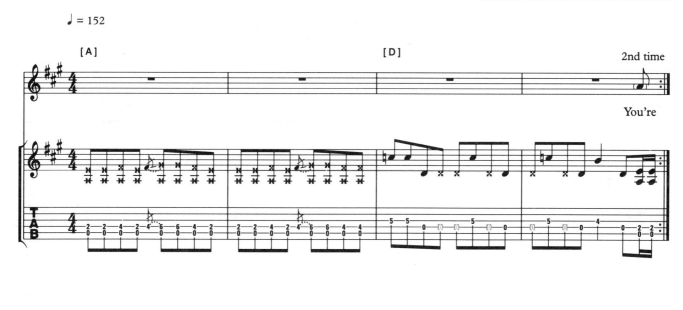

go-ing to a par-ty and you'll ne-ver want to leave it to-night,__ you'll
go-ing to a par-ty and you'll ne-ver want to leave it to-night,__ you'll

wan-na see the band play-ing bish-a bash-a bosh-a to-night.__
wan-na see the band play-ing mu-sic that is push-ing to-night.__

Yeah   whoo hoo!____

To - night.____

Trumpet Solo

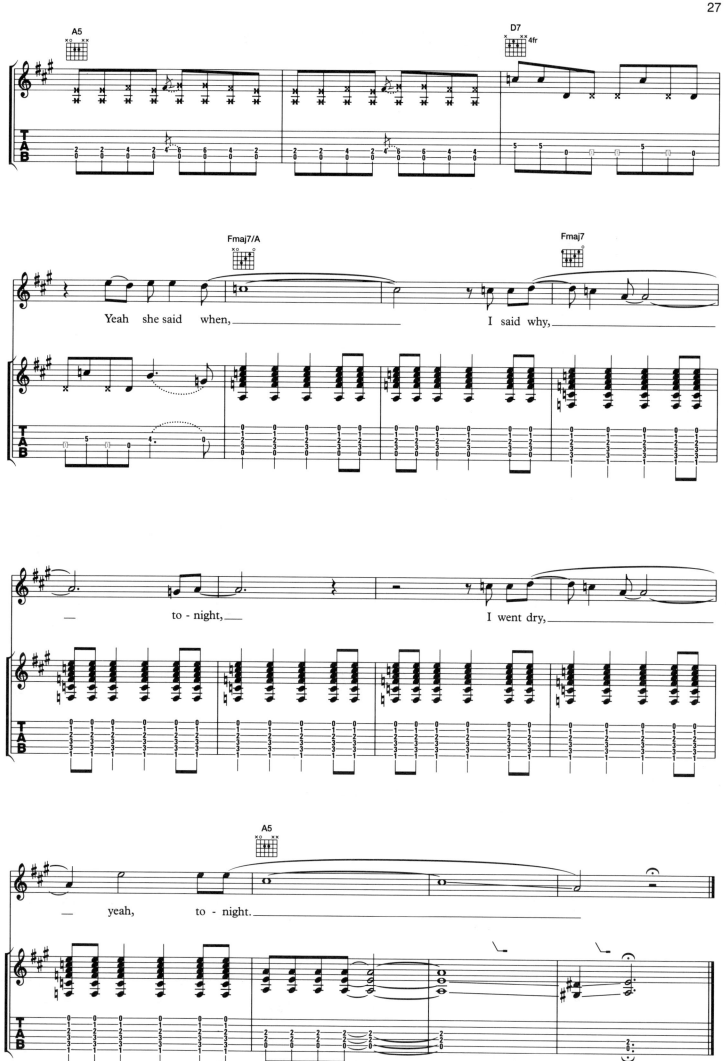

Late In The Day.

Words and Music by
Daniel Goffey, Gareth Coombes,
Michael Quinn and Robert Coombes

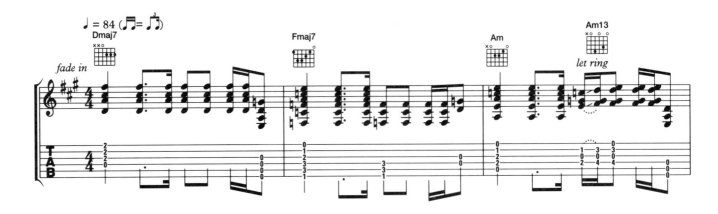

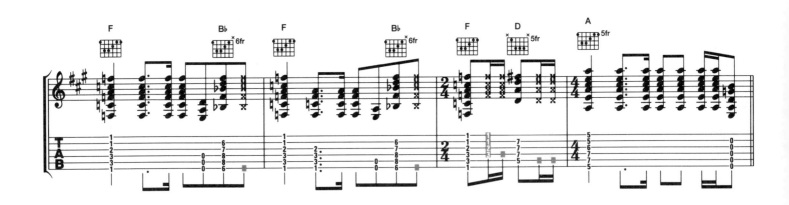

It's late in the day,___ I'm think-ing of you,___ things that you say,___
I lay on my bed___ search-ing my mind,___ light-en my load,

G-Song.

Words and Music by
Daniel Goffey, Gareth Coombes,
Michael Quinn and Robert Coombes

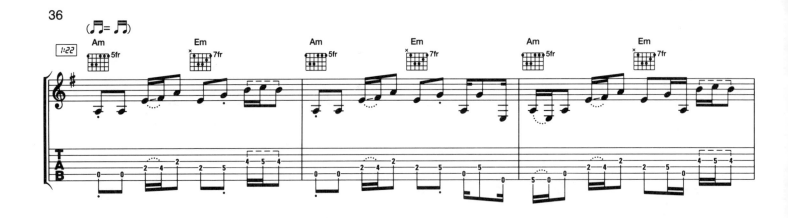

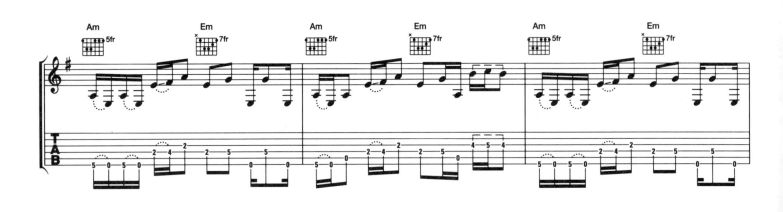

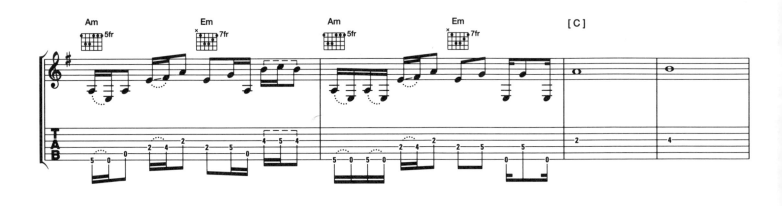

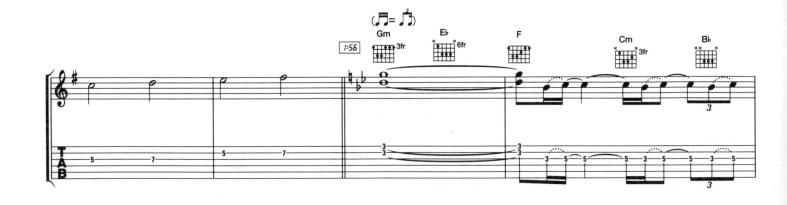

There may be trou-bles in your mind,____ may-be to-mor- row you could be fine.____

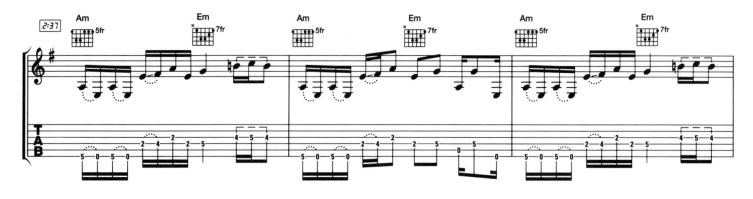

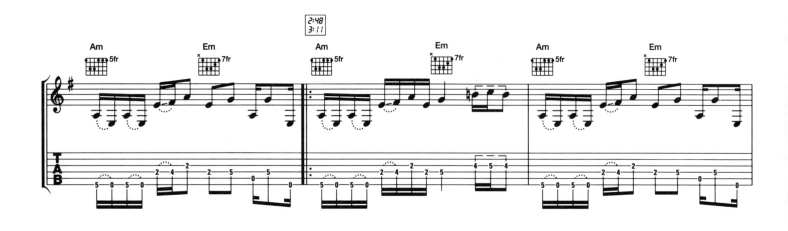

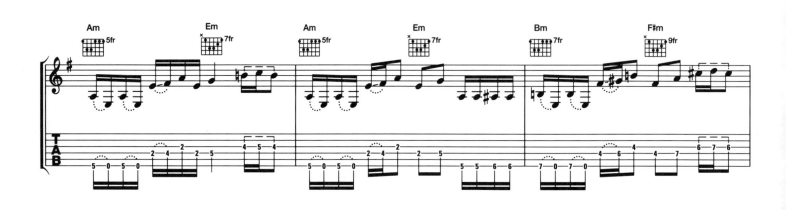

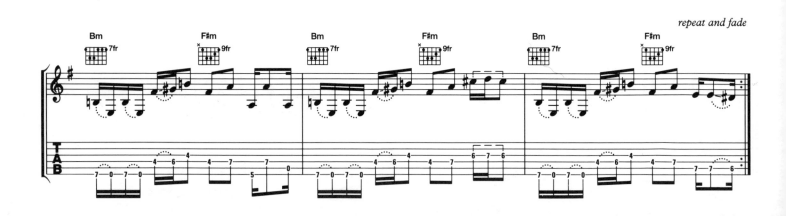

Sun Hits The Sky.

Words and Music by
Daniel Goffey, Gareth Coombes
Michael Quinn and Robert Coombes

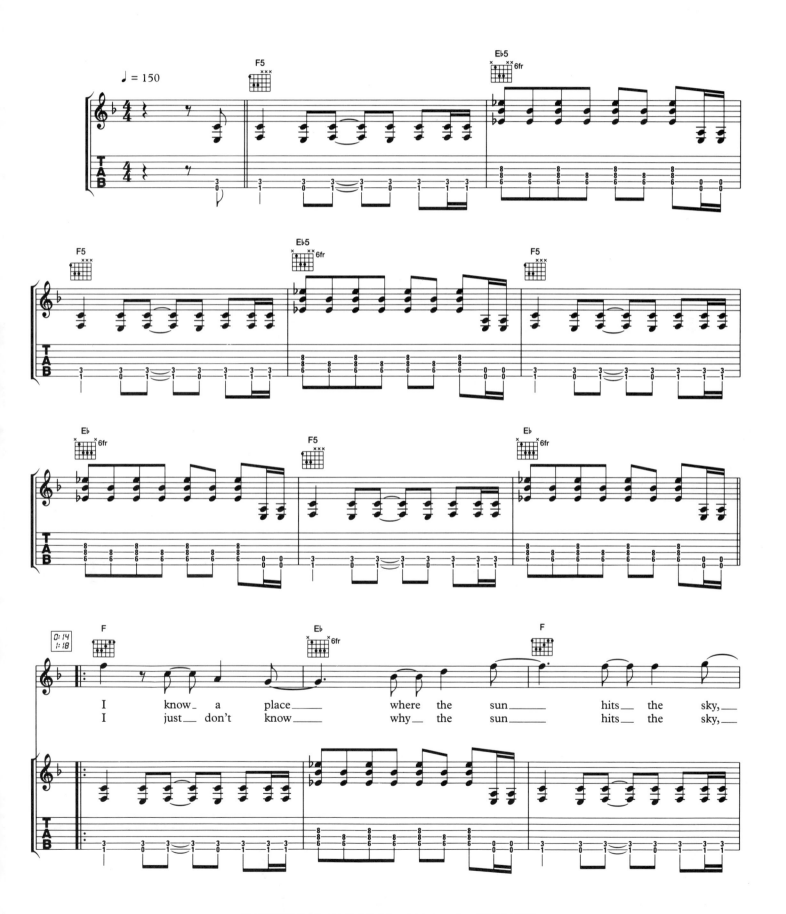

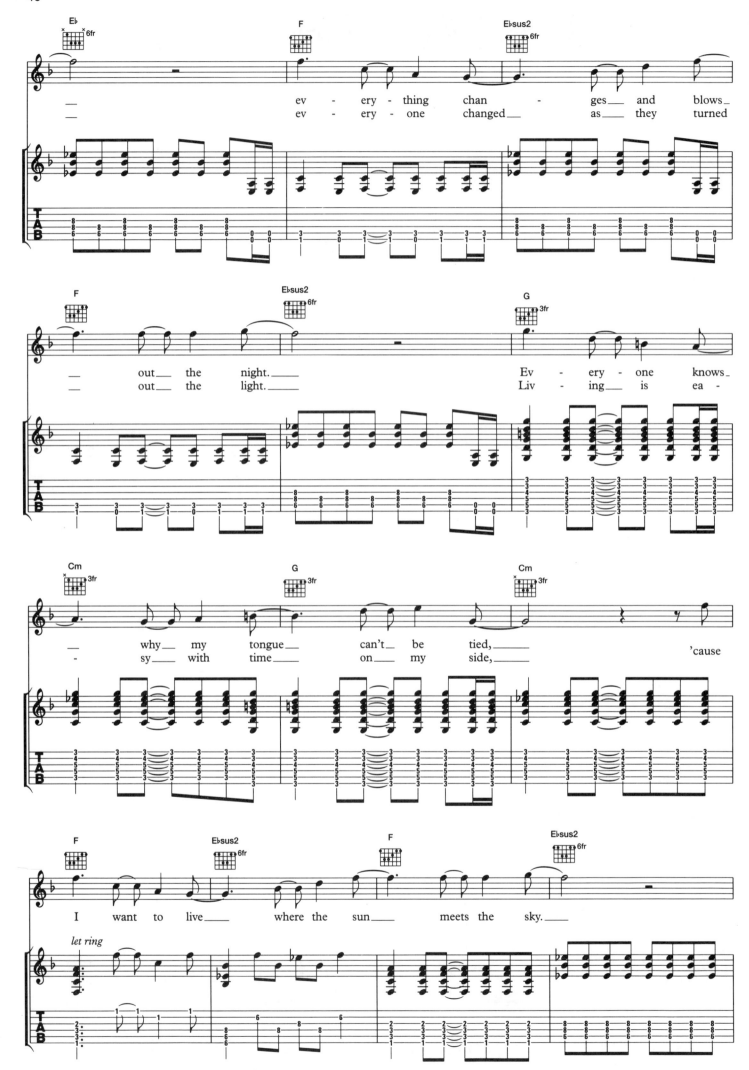

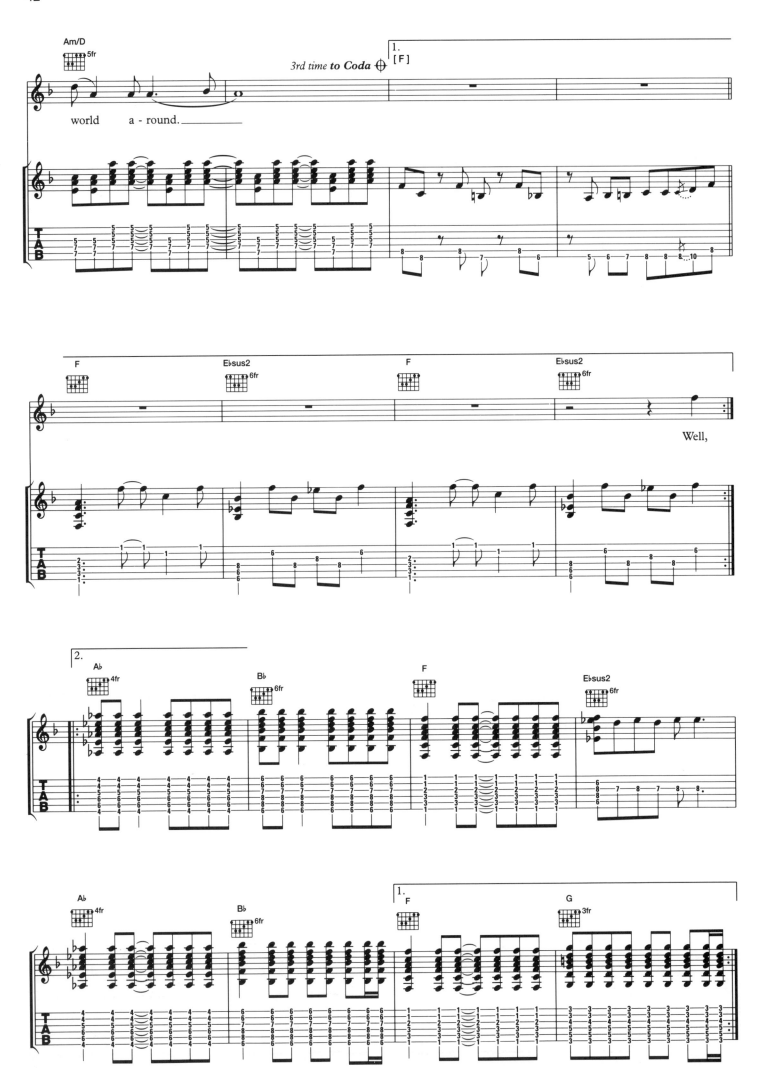

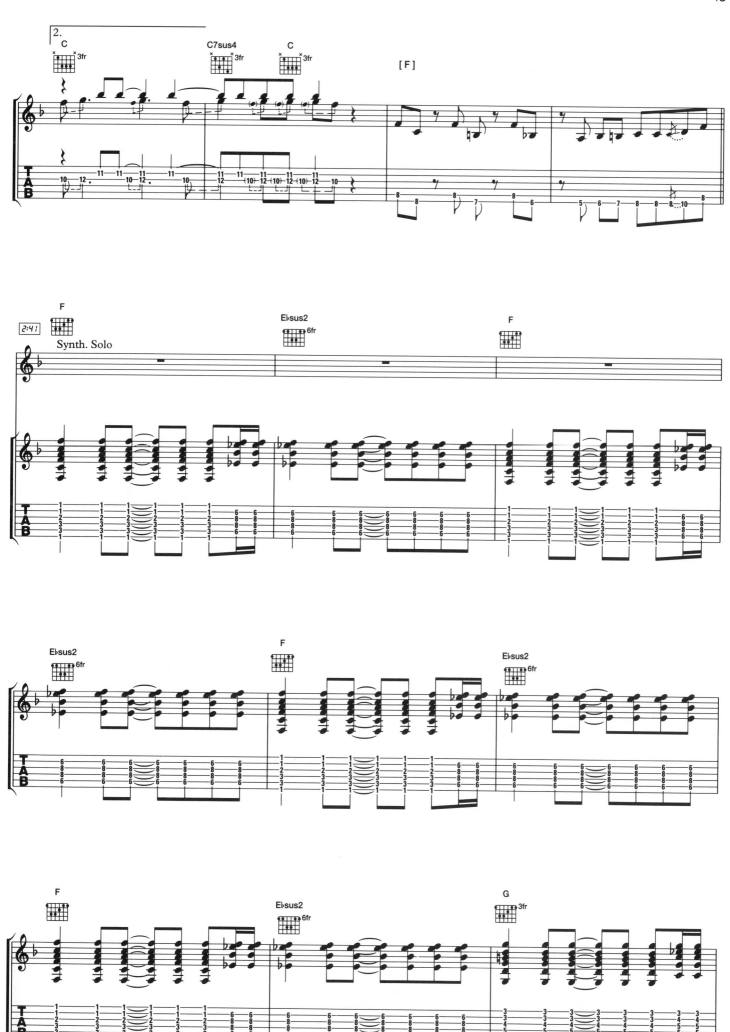

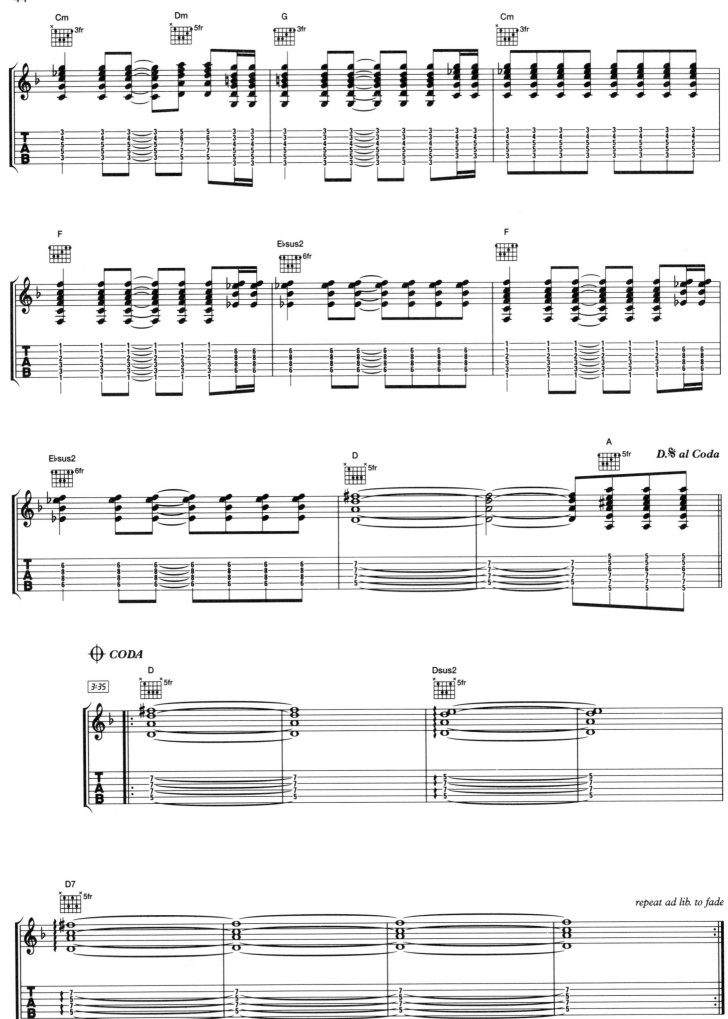

Going Out.

Words and Music by
Daniel Goffey, Gareth Coombes,
Michael Quinn and Robert Coombes

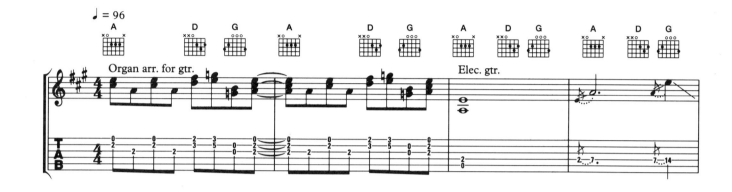

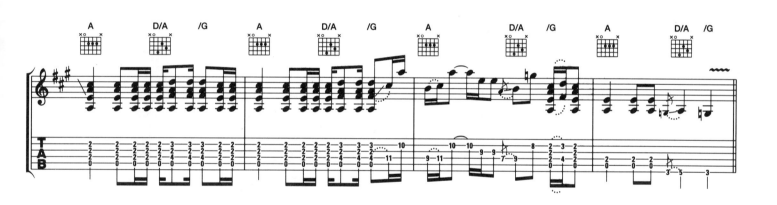

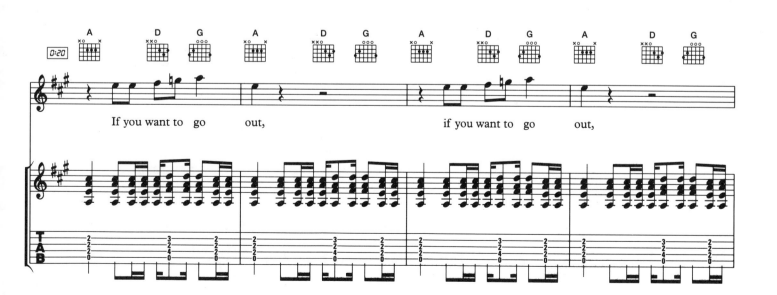

If you want to go out, if you want to go out,

read it in the pa-pers, tell___ me what it's all a-bout,___ yeah.___

If you want to stay home, if you want to stay home,
If you want to play home, if you want to play home,

free-dom of the pa-pers, all___ you ev-er need to know,___ yeah.___
free-dom from the pa-pers, all___ you've got to do is call,___ yeah.___

Free-dom of the pa-pers, all___ you've got to do, oh
Free-dom from the pa-pers, all___ you've got to do, oh

no,   no, _____ oh   no. ___
no,   no, _____ oh   no. ___

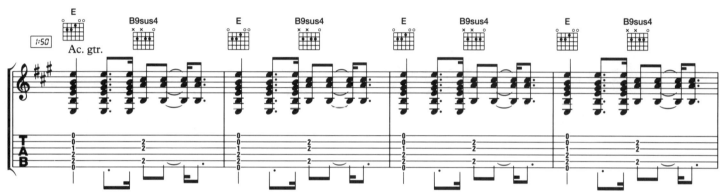

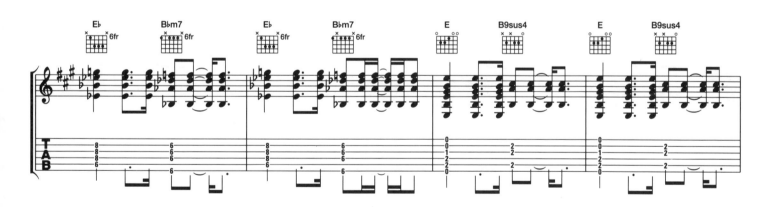

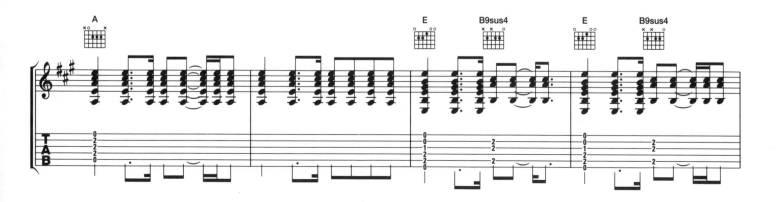

49

If you want to go___ out,   if you want to go___ out.

It's Not Me.

Words and Music by
Daniel Goffey, Gareth Coombes,
Michael Quinn and Robert Coombes

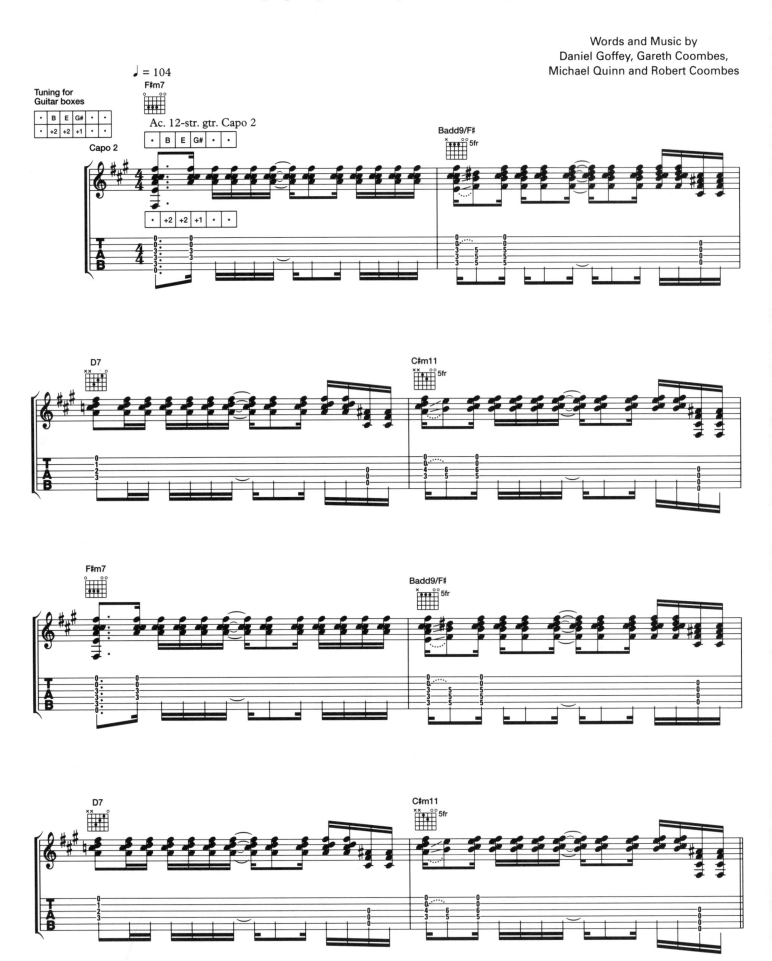

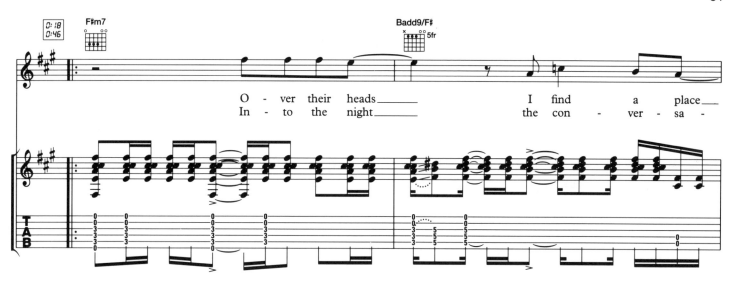

O - ver their heads_____ I find a place_____
In - to the night_____ the con - ver - sa -

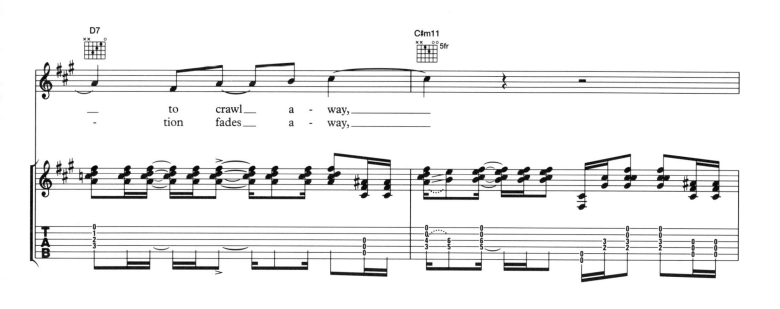

_____ to crawl___ a - way,_____
- tion fades___ a - way,_____

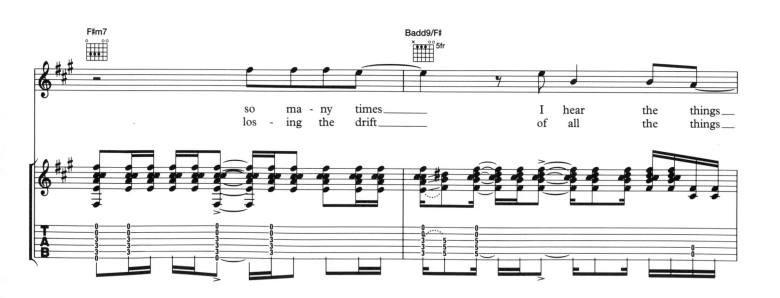

so ma - ny times_____ I hear the things_____
los - ing the drift_____ of all the things_____

we used__ to say._____
I had__ to say._____

It's not me,___ no no_____ not me___ but I____

Cheapskate.

Words and Music by
Daniel Goffey, Gareth Coombes,
Michael Quinn and Robert Coombes

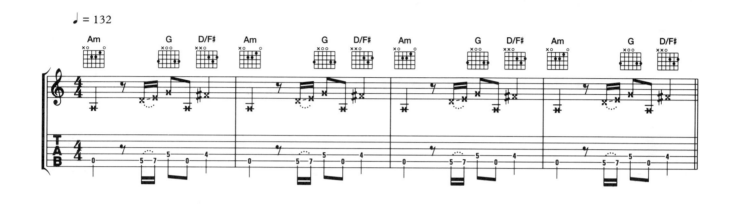

Lift me up____ and move in clos- er,

hold -ing on____ to what I know.____

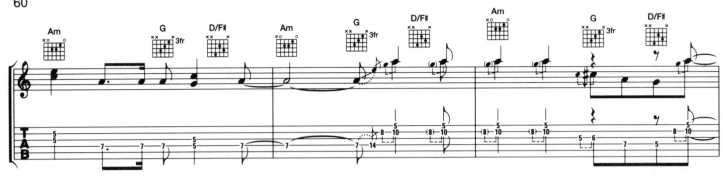

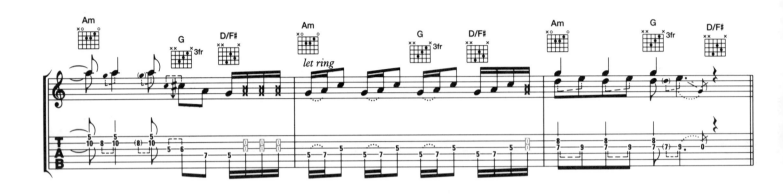

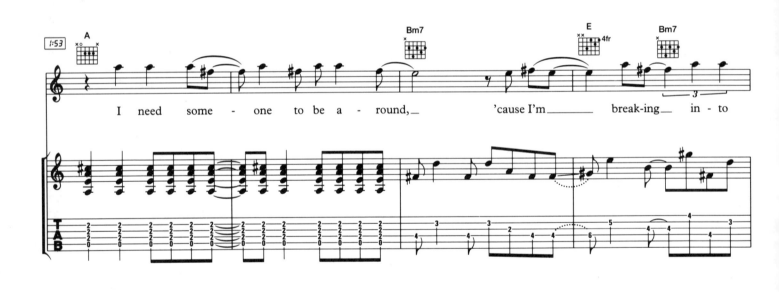

I need some - one to be a - round,   'cause I'm   break-ing in - to

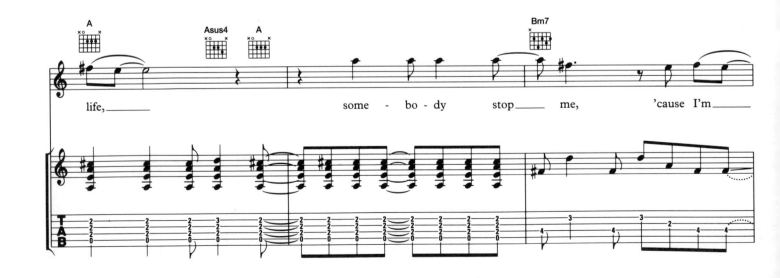

life,   some - bo - dy   stop   me,   'cause I'm

repeat and fade

You Can See Me.

Words and Music by
Daniel Goffey, Gareth Coombes,
Michael Quinn and Robert Coombes

If you like me, you can buy me and
When you need me, come and see me and

take me home,
take me out,

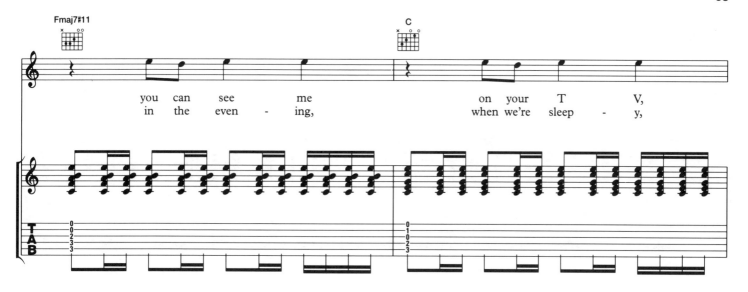

you can see me   on your T V,
in the even - ing,   when we're sleep - y,

I'm   a - lone,_____
lay   me down,_____

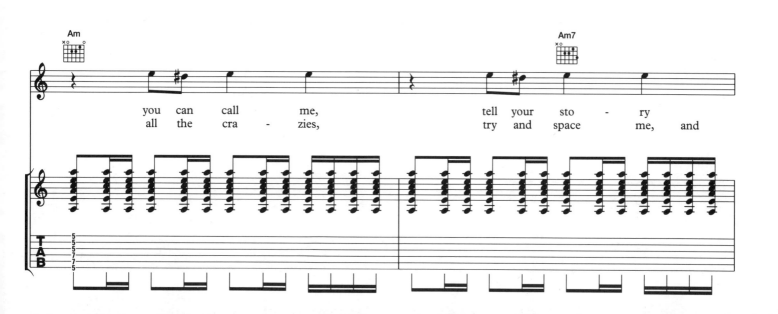

you can call me,   tell your sto - ry
all the cra - zies,   try and space me, and

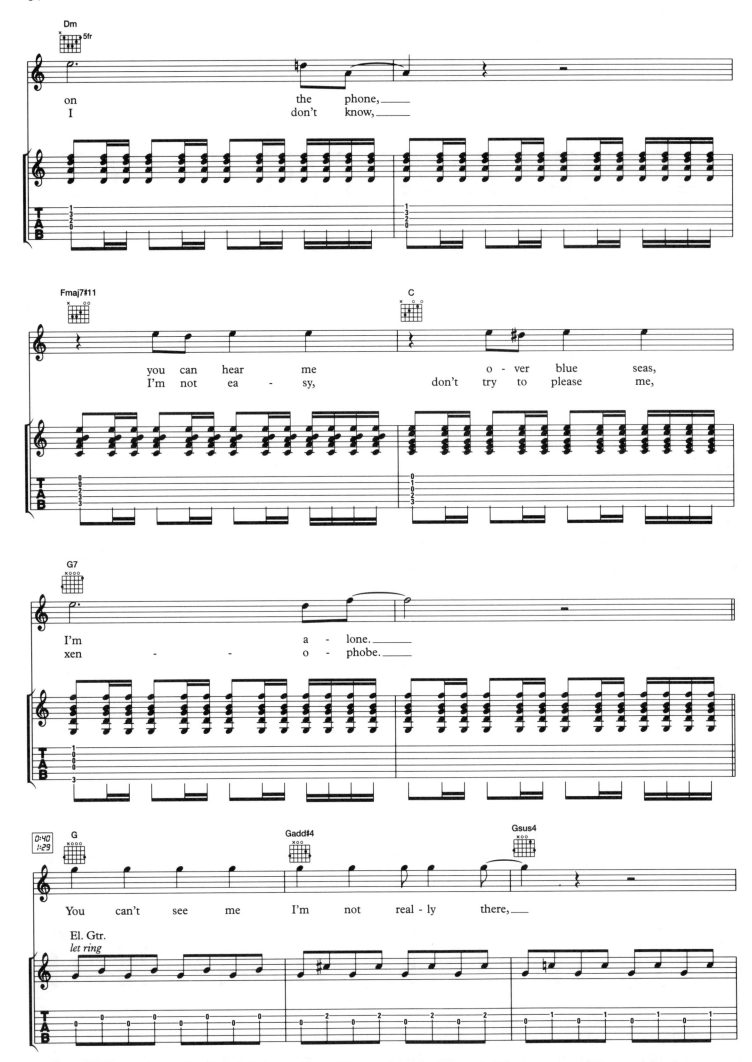

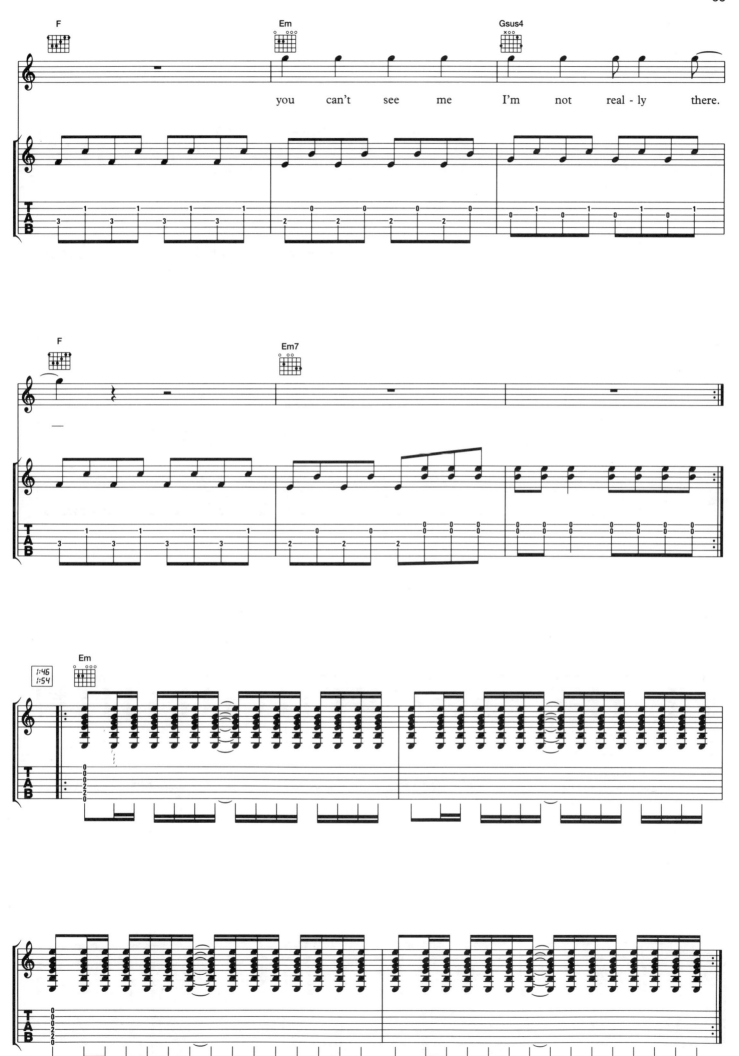

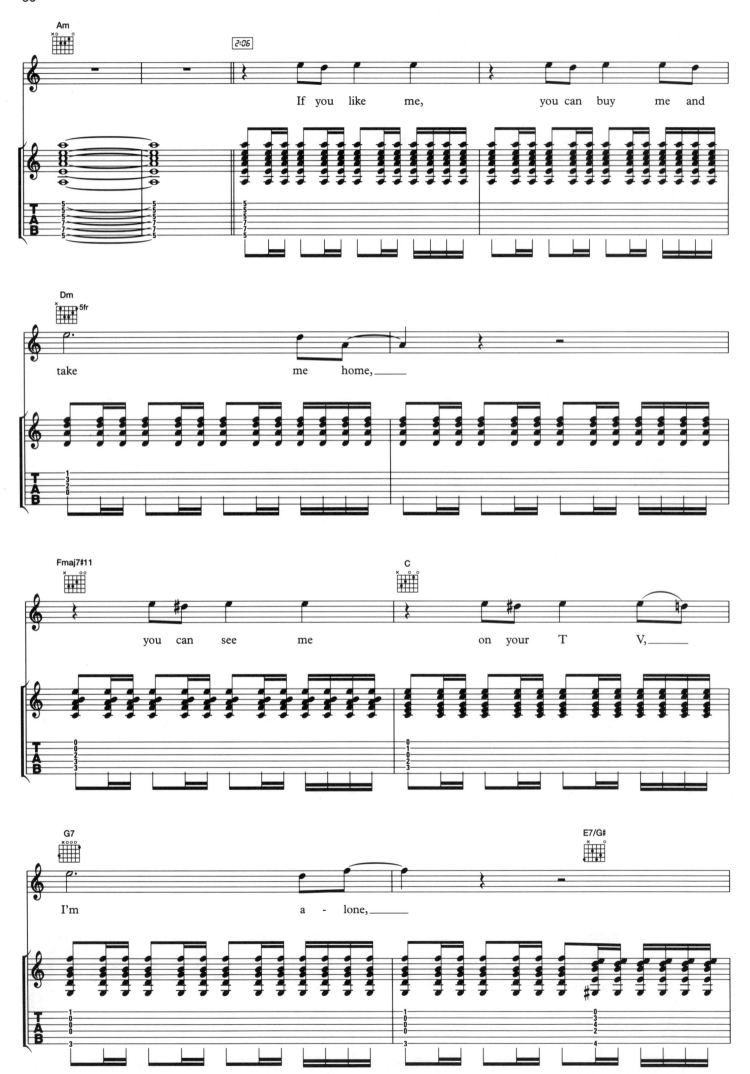

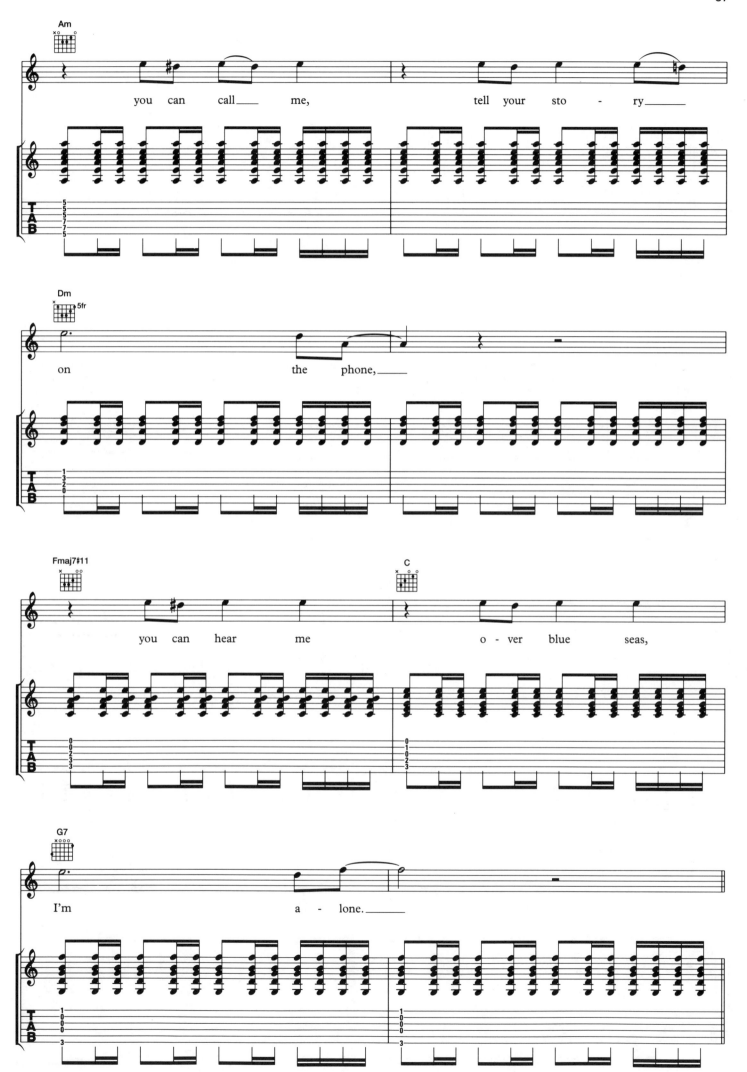

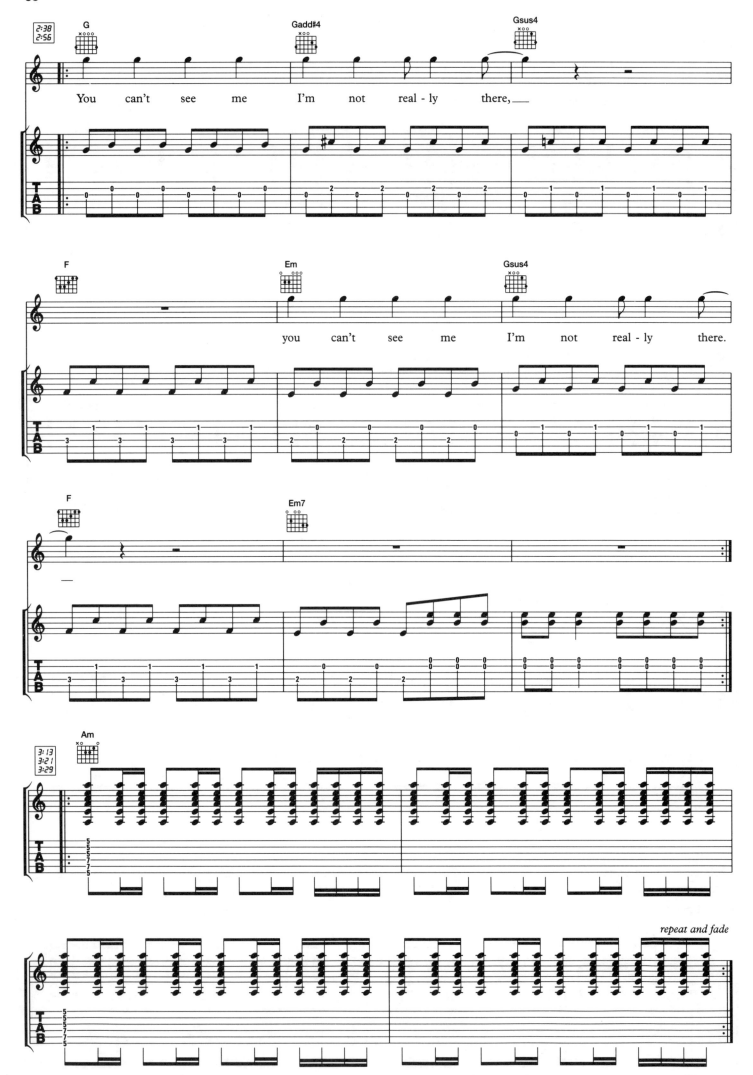

Hollow Little Reign.

Words and Music by
Daniel Goffey, Gareth Coombes,
Michael Quinn and Robert Coombes

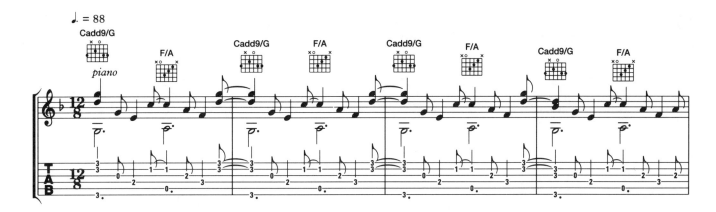

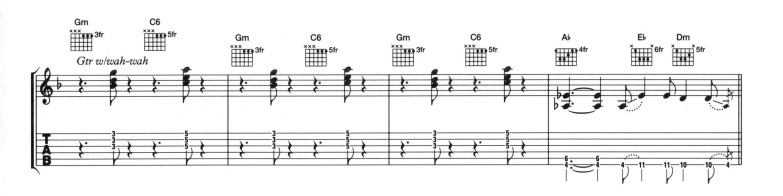

Up - tight___ think - ing things o - ver,___ con - ver - sa - tions run - ning
Cool skies drink - ing the sun - shine, feel the wind blow - ing
Some - times clouds will come o - ver,___ leo - pard spots in

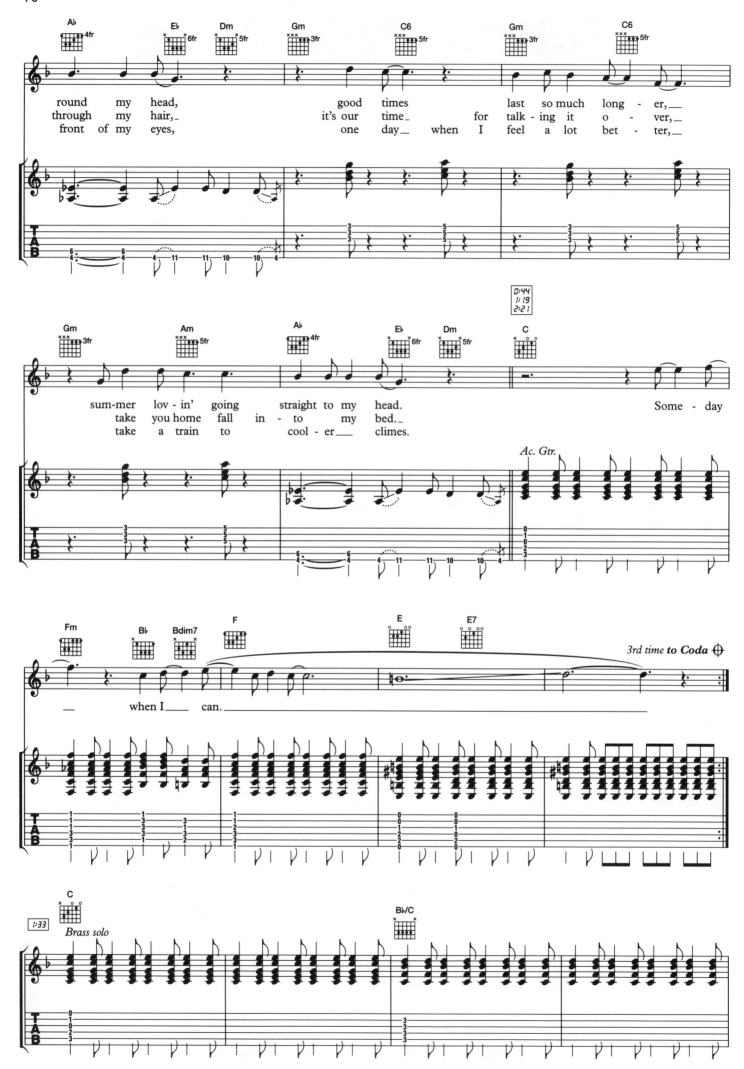

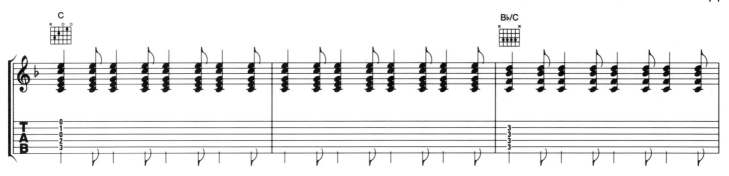

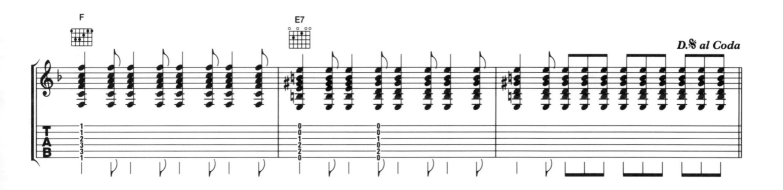

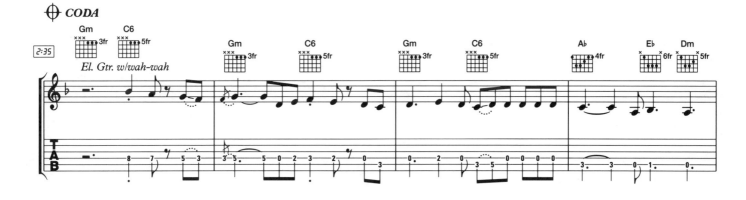

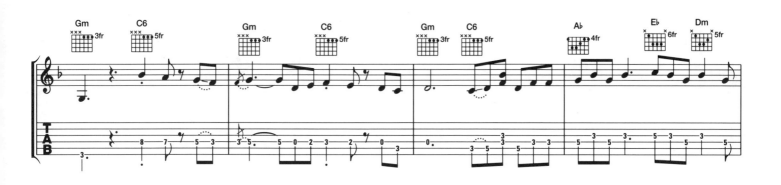

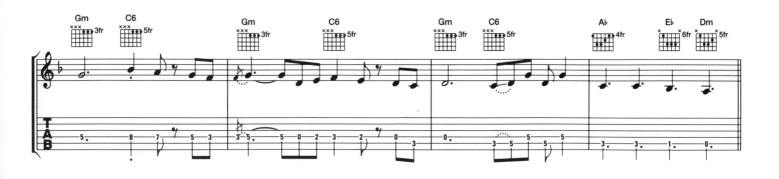

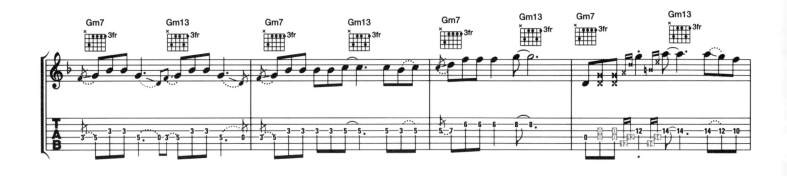

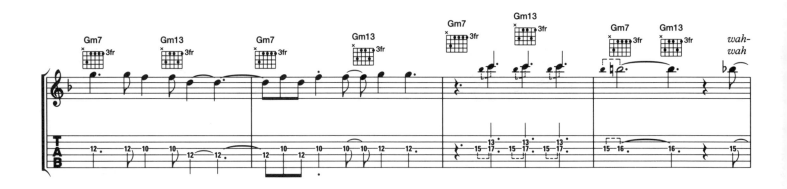

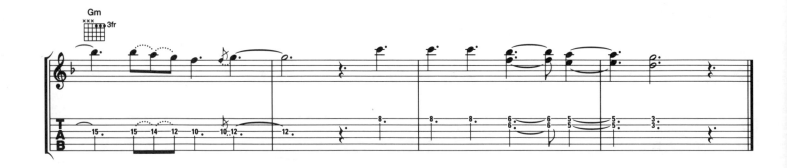

Sometimes I Make You Sad.

Words and Music by
Daniel Goffey, Gareth Coombes,
Michael Quinn and Robert Coombes

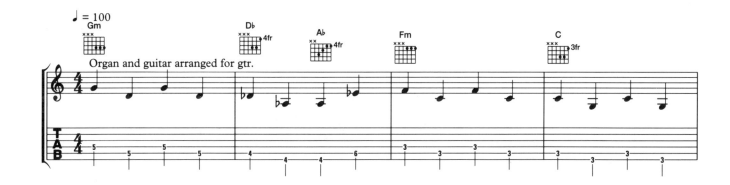

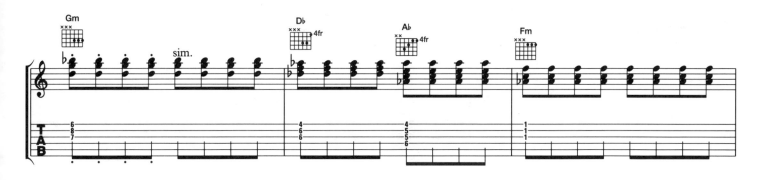

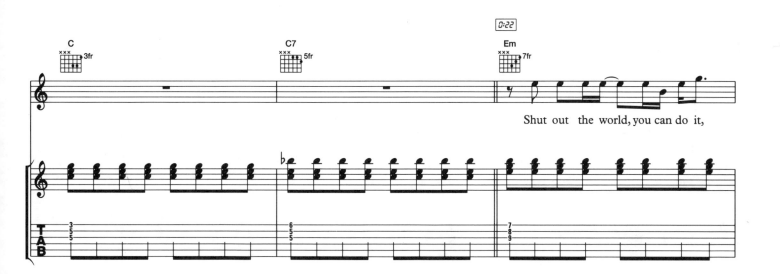

Shut out the world, you can do it,

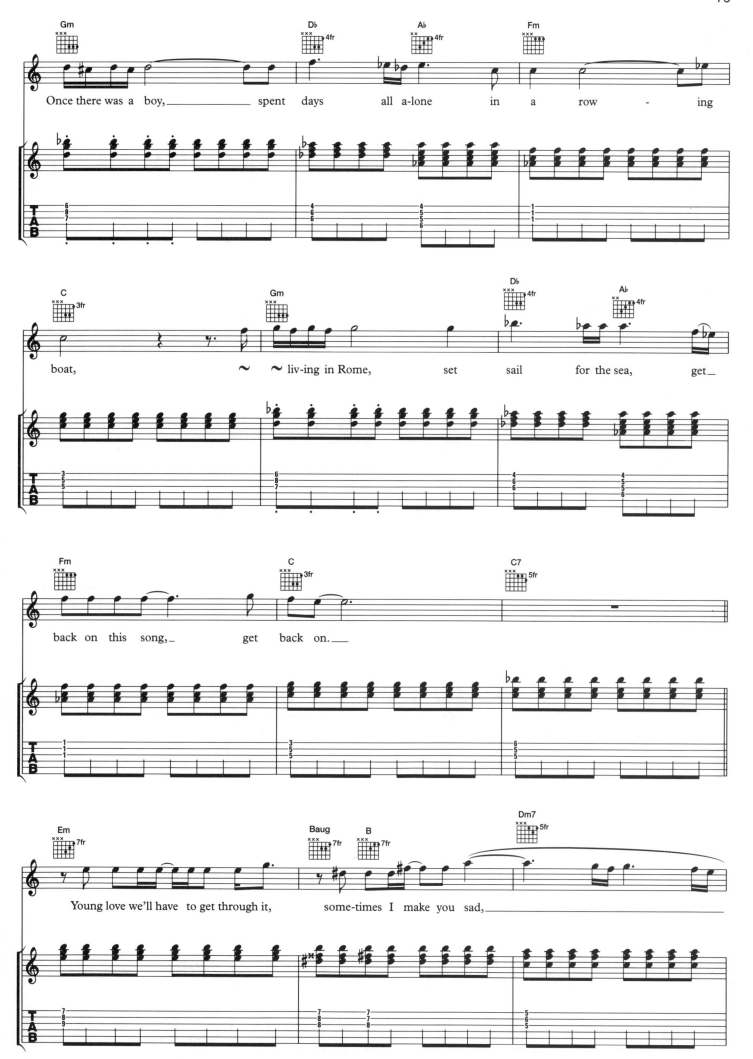

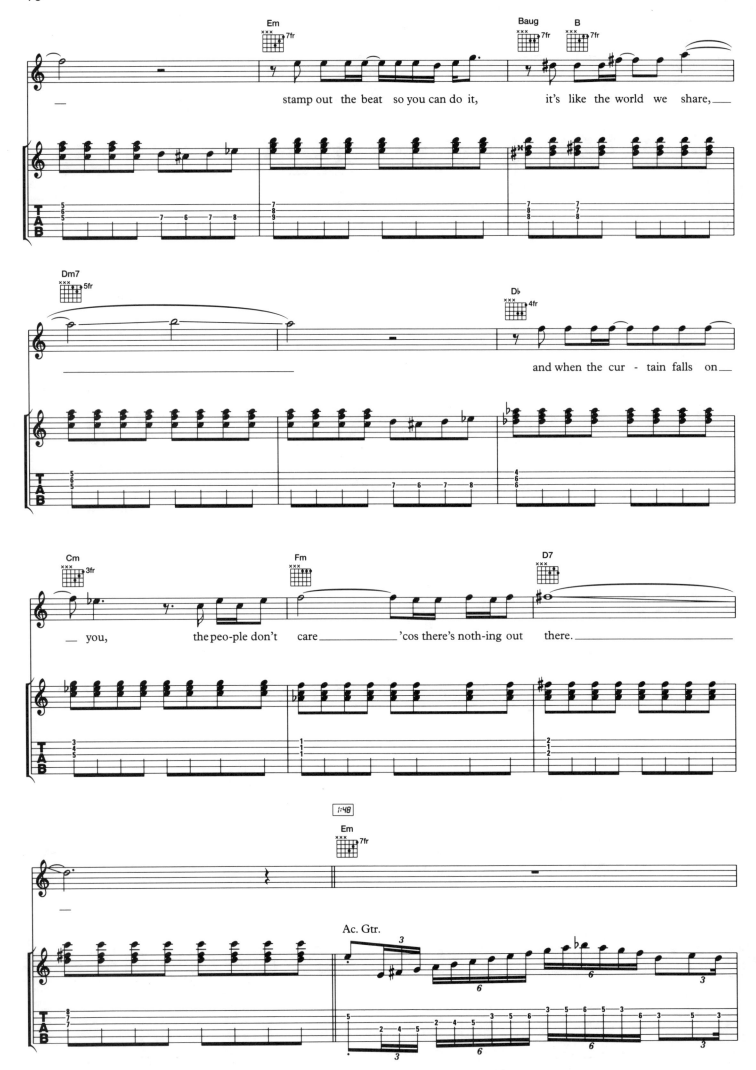

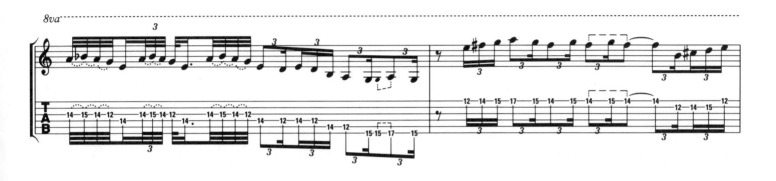

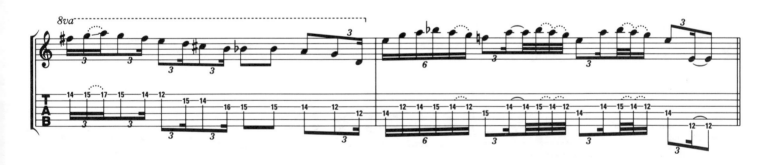

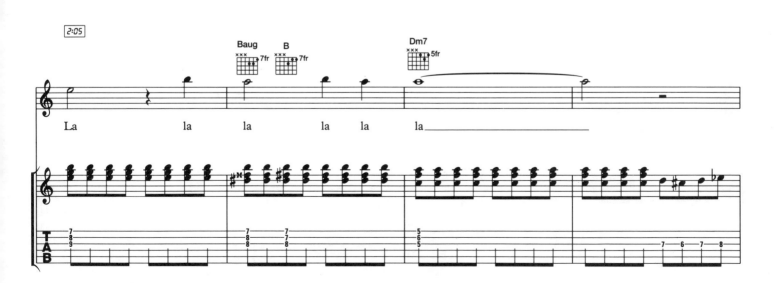

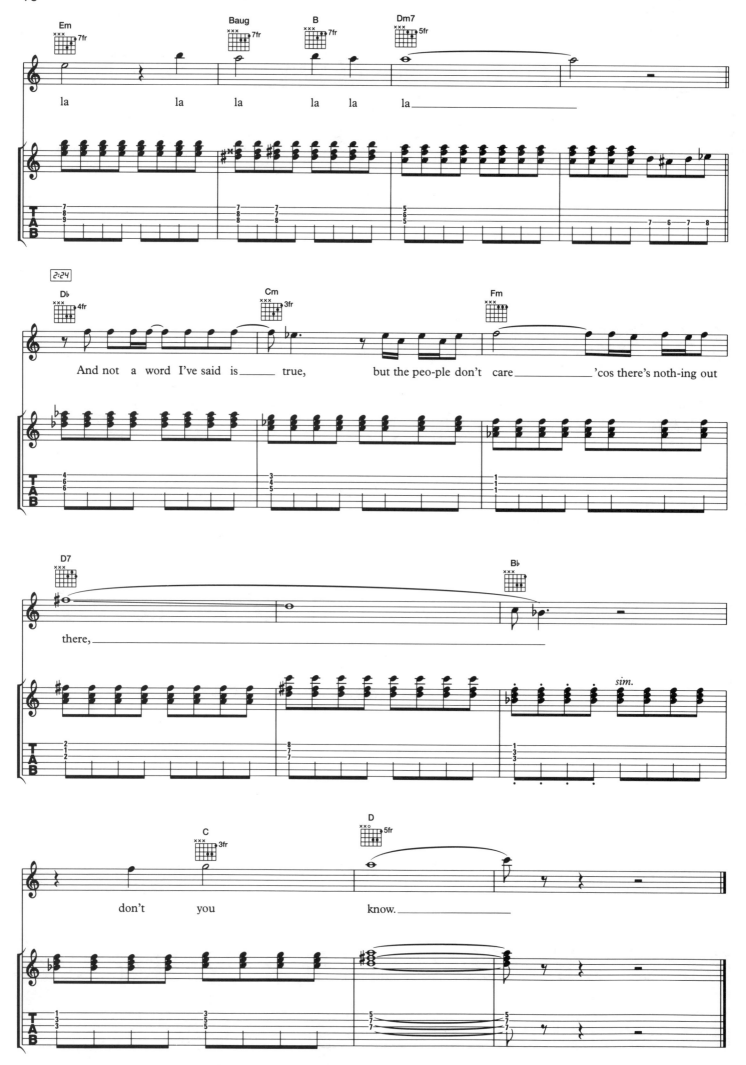

Notation and Tablature Explained

Open C chord

Scale of E major

High E (1st) string
B (2nd) string
G (3rd) string
D (4th) string
A (5th) string
Low E (6th) string

Bent Notes

The note fretted is always shown first. Variations in pitch achieved by string bending are enclosed within this symbol ⌐ ⌐. If you aren't sure how far to bend the string, playing the notes indicated without bending gives a guide to the pitches to aim for. The following examples cover the most common string bending techniques:

Example 1
Play the D, bend up one tone (two half-steps) to E.

Example 2
Play the D, bend up one tone to E then release bend to sound D. Only the first note is picked.

Example 3
Fast bend: Play the D, then bend up one tone to E as quickly as possible.

Example 4
Pre-bend: fret the D, bend up one tone to E, then pick.

Example 5
Play the A and D together, then bend the B-string up one tone to sound B.

Example 6
Play the D and F# together, then bend the G-string up one tone to E, and the B-string up a semitone to G.

Additional guitaristic techniques have been notated as follows:

Tremolo Bar
Alter pitch using tremolo bar. Where possible, the pitch to aim for is shown.
a) Play the G; use the bar to drop the pitch to E.
b) Play the open G; use the bar to 'divebomb', i.e. drop the pitch as far as possible.

Hammer on and Pull off
Play first note, sound next note by 'hammering on', the next by 'pulling off'. Only the first note is picked.

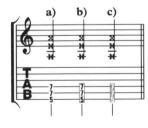

Mutes
a) Right hand mute
Mute strings by resting the right hand on the strings just above the bridge.
b) Left hand mute
Damp the strings by releasing left hand pressure just after the notes sound.
c) Unpitched mute
Damp the strings with the left hand to produce a percussive sound.

Glissando
a) Play first note, sound next note by sliding up string. Only the first note is picked.
b) As above, but pick second note.

Natural Harmonics
Touch the string over the fret marked, and pick to produce a bell-like tone. The small notes show the resultant pitch, where necessary.

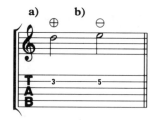

Slide Guitar
a) Play using slide.
b) Play without slide.

Artificial Harmonics
Fret the lowest note, touch string over fret indicated by diamond notehead and pick. Small notes show the resultant pitch.

Vibrato
Apply vibrato, by 'shaking' note or with tremolo bar. As vibrato is so much a matter of personal taste and technique, it is indicated only where essential.

Pinch Harmonics
Fret the note as usual, but 'pinch' or 'squeeze' the string with the picking hand to produce a harmonic overtone. Small notes show the resultant pitch.

Pick Scratch
Scrape the pick down the strings – this works best on the wound strings.

Microtones
A downwards arrow means the written pitch is lowered by less than a semitone; an upwards arrow raises the written pitch.

Repeated Chords
To make rhythm guitar parts easier to read the tablature numbers may be omitted when a chord is repeated. The example shows a C major chord played naturally, r/h muted, l/h muted and as an unpitched mute respectively.

Special Tunings
Non-standard tunings are shown as 'tuning boxes'. Each box represents one guitar string, the leftmost box corresponding to the lowest pitched string. The symbol '•' in a box means the pitch of the corresponding string is not altered. A note within a box means the string must be re-tuned as stated. For tablature readers, numbers appear in the boxes. The numbers represent the number of half-steps the string must be tuned up or down. The tablature relates to an instrument tuned as stated.

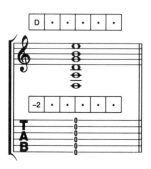

Tune the low E (6th) string down one tone (two half-steps) to D.

Chord naming
The following chord naming convention has been used:

Where there is no appropriate chord box, for example when the music consists of a repeated figure (or riff) the tonal base is indicated in parenthesis: [C]

Where it was not possible to transcribe a passage, the symbol ∼ appears.

Indications sur la notation musicale et les tablatures

Accord de Do majeur ouvert

Gamme de Mi majeur

Mi aigu: 1ère corde
Si: 2e corde
Sol: 3e corde
Ré: 4e corde
La: 5e corde
Mi grave: 6e corde

Bending

La note correspondant à la case sur laquelle on pose le doigt est toujours indiquée en premier. Les variations de hauteur sont obtenues en poussant sur la corde et sont indiquées par le symbole: ⌐ ¬. En cas de doute sur la hauteur à atteindre, le fait de jouer les notes indiquées sans pousser sur la corde permet de trouver ensuite la bonne hauteur. Les examples suivants démontrent les techniques de bending les plus courantes.

Exemple 1
Jouez la note Ré et poussez la corde d'un ton (deux demi-tons) pour atteindre le Mi.

Exemple 4
'Pre-bend': posez le doigt sur la case de Ré, poussez d'un ton pour atteindre le Mi avant de jouer la note.

Exemple 2
Jouez le Ré, poussez sur la corde pour atteindre le Mi un ton plus haut, relâchez ensuite pour revenir au Ré. Seule la première note est jouée avec le médiator.

Exemple 5
Jouez La et Ré simultanément; poussez ensuite sur la corde de Si pour atteindre la note Si.

Exemple 3
'Fast Bend': jouez le Ré et poussez le plus rapidement possible pour atteindre le Mi.

Exemple 6
Jouez Ré et Fa# simultanément; poussez la corde de Sol d'un ton vers le Mi, et la corde de Si d'un demi-ton vers le Sol.

D'autres techniques de guitare sont notées de la façon suivante:

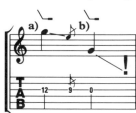

Emploi du levier de vibrato
Modifiez la hauteur du son avec le levier de vibrato. Lorsque c'est possible, la note à atteindre est indiquée.
a) Jouez le Sol et appuyez sur le levier de vibrato pour atteindre le Mi.
b) Jouez un Sol à vide et détendez le plus possible la corde avec le levier de vibrato pour rendre un effect de 'bombe qui tombe' (divebomb).

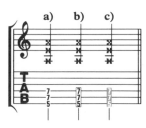

Mutes (étouffements)
a) Mute de la main droite
Etouffez en posant la main droite sur les cordes, au-dessus du chevalet.
b) Mute de la main gauche
Relâchez la pression sur la corde juste après avoir joué la note.
c) Mute sans hauteur définie
Etouffez les cordes avec la main gauche pour obtenir un son de percussion.

Hammer On et Pull Off
Jouez la première note; frappez la corde sur la touche (Hammer On) pour obtenir la seconde note, et relâchez la seconde note en tirant sur la corde (Pull Off) pour obtenir la troisième note. Seule la première note est donc jouée avec le médiator.

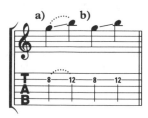

Glissando
a) Jouez la première note avec le médiator, faites sonner la seconde note en ne faisant que glisser le doigt sur la corde.
b) Comme ci-dessus, mais en attaquant également la seconde note avec le médiator.

Harmoniques naturelles

Posez le doigt sur la corde au dessus de la barrette indiquée, et jouez avec le médiator pour obtenir un son cristallin. Le cas échéant, une petite note indique la hauteur du son que l'on doit obtenir.

Guitare Slide

a) Note jouée avec le slide.
b) Note jouée sans le slide.

Harmoniques artificielles

Posez le doigt (main gauche) sur la note la plus basse: effleurez la corde avec l'index de la main droite au-dessus de la barrette indiquée par la note en forme de losange, tout en actionnant le médiator. La petite note indique la hauteur du son que l'on doit obtenir.

Effet de Vibrato

Jouez le vibrato soit avec le doigt sur la corde (main gauche), soit avec le levier de vibrato. Comme le vibrato est une affaire de technique et de goût personnels, il n'est indiqué que quand cela est vraiment nécessaire.

Harmoniques pincées

Appuyez le doigt sur la corde de la façon habituelle, mais utilisez conjointement le médiator et l'index de la main droite de façon á obtenir une harmonique aiguě. Les petites notes indiquent la hauteur du son que l'on doit obtenir.

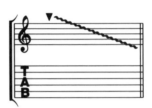

Scratch

Faites glisser le médiator du haut en bas de la corde. Le meilleur effet est obtenu avec des cordes filetées.

Quarts de ton

Une flèche dirigée vers le bas indique que la note est baissée d'un quart-de-ton. Une flèche dirigée vers le haut indique que la note est haussée d'un quart-de-ton.

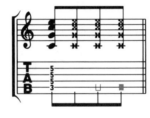

Accords répétés

Pour faciliter la lecture des parties de guitare rythmique, les chiffres de tablature sont omis quand l'accord est répété. L'example montre successivement un accord de Do majeur joué de façon normale, un 'mute' de la main droite, un 'mute' de la main gauche et un 'mute' sans hauteur définie.

Accordages spéciaux

Les accordages non-standards sont indiqués par six cases, chacune représentant une corde (de gauche à droite), de la plus grave à la plus aiguë. Un tiret indique que la tension de la corde correspondante ne doit pas être altérée. Un nom de note indique la nouvelle note à obtenir. Pour les tablatures, les chiffres indiqués dans les cases représentent le nombre de demi-tons dont ou doit désaccorder la corde, vers le haut ou vers le bas.

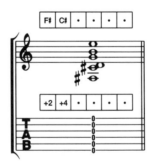

Accordez la corde de Mi grave un ton plus haut de façon à obtenir un Fa#, et la corde de La deux tons plus haut de façon à obtenir un Do#.

Noms des accords

Lorsqu'aucun nom d'accord précis n'est applicable, par exemple quand la musique consiste en une figure répétée (riff), le centre tonal est indiqué entre parenthèses: [C]

Lorsqu'un passage n'a pas pu être transcrit, le symbole ~ apparait.

Hinweise zu Notation und Tabulatur

Offener C - Dur - Akkord

E - Dur - Tonleiter

Hohe E-Saite (1.)
H-Saite (2.)
G-Saite (3.)
D-Saite (4.)
A-Saite (5.)
Tiefe E-Saite (6.)

Gezogene Noten

Die gegriffene Note wird immer zuerst angegeben. Das Zeichen ⌐ ¬ zeigt eine Veränderung der Tonhöhe an, die durch das Ziehen der Saiten erreicht wird. Falls Du nicht sicher bist, wie weit die Saite gezogen werden soll, spiele die entsprechenden Töne zunächst ohne Ziehen; so kannst Du Dich an der Tonhöhe orientieren. Die folgenden Beispiele geben die gebräuchlichsten Techniken zum Ziehen wieder:

Beispiel 1
Spiele das D und ziehe dann um einen Ton (zwei Halbtonschritte) höher zum E.

Beispiel 4
Im Voraus gezogen: Greife das D, ziehe um einen Ton höher zum E und schlage erst dann die Saite an.

Beispiel 2
Spiele das D, ziehe um einen Ton hoch zum E und dann wieder zurück, so daß D erklingt. Dabei wird nur die erste Note angeschlagen.

Beispiel 5
Spiele A und D gleichzeitig und ziehe dann die H-Saite um einen Ton nach oben, so daß H erklingt.

Beispiel 3
Schnelles Ziehen: Spiele das D und ziehe dann so schnell Du kannst um einen Ton höher zum E.

Beispiel 6
Spiele D und Fis gleichzeitig; ziehe dann die G-Saite um einen Ton nach oben zum E und die H-Saite um einen Halbtonschritt nach oben zum G.

Zusätzliche Spieltechniken für Gitarre wurden folgendermaßen notiert:

Tremolo
Verändere die Tonhöhe mit dem Tremolo-Hebel. Wenn es möglich ist, wird die angestrebte Tonhöhe angezeigt.
a) Spiele G; nutze den Takt, um zum E abzusteigen.
b) Spiele die leere G-Saite; nutze den Takt, um so weit wie möglich abzusteigen.

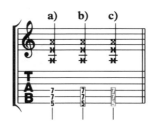

Dämpfen
a) Mit der rechten Hand
Dämpfe die Saiten, indem Du die rechte Hand einfach oberhalb der Brücke auf die Saiten legst.
b) Mit der linken Hand
Dämpfe die Saiten, indem Du den Druck der linken Hand löst, kurz nachdem die Töne erklingen.
c) Ohne bestimmte Tonhöhe
Dämpfe die Saiten mit der linken Hand; so erzielst Du einen 'geschlagenen' Sound.

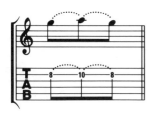

Hammer on und Pull off
Spiele die erste Note; die zweite erklingt durch 'Hammering on', die dritte durch 'Pulling off'. Dabei wird nur die erste Note angeschlagen.

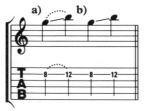

Glissando
a) Spiele die erste Note; die zweite erklingt durch Hochrutschen des Fingers auf der Saite. Nur die erste Note wird angeschlagen.
b) Wie oben, aber die zweite Note wird angeschlagen.

Natürliches Flageolett
Berühre die Saite über dem angegebenen Bund; wenn Du jetzt anschlägst, entsteht ein glockenähnlicher Ton. Wo es nötig ist, zeigen kleine Notenköpfe die entstandene Note an.

Slide Guitar
a) Spiele mit Rutschen des Fingers.
b) Spiele ohne Rutschen.

Künstliches Flageolett
Greife die unterste Note, berühre die Saite über dem durch Rauten angegebenen Bund und schlage dann den Ton an. Die kleinen Notenköpfe zeigen wieder die entstandene Note an.

Vibrato
Beim Vibrato läßt Du die Note für die Dauer eines Tons durch Druckvariation oder Tremolo-Hebel 'beben'. Da es jedoch eine Frage des persönlichen Geschmacks ist, wird Vibrato nur dort angegeben, wo es unerläßlich ist.

Gezupftes Flageolett
Greife die Note ganz normal, aber drücke die Saite mit der zupfenden Hand so, daß ein harmonischer Oberton entsteht. Kleine Notenköpfe zeigen den entstandenen Ton an.

Pick Scratch
Fahre mit dem Plektrum nach unten über die Saiten – das klappt am besten bei umsponnenen Saiten.

Vierteltöne
Ein nach unten gerichteter Pfeil bedeutet, daß die notierte Tonhöhe um einen Viertelton erniedrigt wird; ein nach oben gerichteter Pfeil bedeutet, daß die notierte Tonhöhe um einen Viertelton erhöht wird.

Akkordwiederholung
Um die Stimmen für Rhythmus-Gitarre leichter lesbar zu machen, werden die Tabulaturziffern weggelassen, wenn ein Akkord wiederholt werden soll. Unser Beispiel zeigt einen C - Dur - Akkord normal gespielt, rechts gedämpft, links gedämpft und ohne Tonhöhe.

Besondere Stimmung
Falls eine Stimmung verlangt wird, die vom Standard abweicht, wird sie in Kästchen angegeben. Jedes Kästchen steht für eine Saite, das erste links außen entspricht der tiefsten Saite. Wenn die Tonhöhe einer Saite nicht verändert werden soll, enthält das Kästchen einen Punkt. Steht eine Note im Kästchen, muß die Saite wie angegeben umgestimmt werden. In der Tabulaturschrift stehen stattdessen Ziffern im entsprechenden Kästchen: Sie geben die Zahl der Halbtonschritte an, um die eine Saite höher oder tiefer gestimmt werden soll.

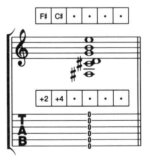

Stimme die tiefe E-Saite (6.) um einen Ganzton (zwei Halbtonschritte) höher auf Fis und die A-Saite (5.) um zwei Ganztöne (vier Halbtonschritte) höher auf Cis.

Akkordbezeichnung
Die folgenden Akkordbezeichnungen wurden verwendet.

Wenn kein eigenes Akkordsymbol angegeben ist, z.B. bei Wiederholung einer musikalischen Figur (bzw. Riff), steht die Harmoniebezeichnung in Klammern: [C]

Das Symbol ~ steht jeweils dort, wo es nicht möglich war, einen Abschnitt zu übertragen.

Spiegazione della notazione e dell'intavolatura

Accordo di Do aperto
(in prima posizione)

Scala di Mi maggiore

Mi acuto: la corda
Si: 2a corda
Sol: 3a corda
Re: 4a corda
La: 5a corda
Mi basso: 6a corda

Bending

La prima nota scritta è sempre quella tastata normalmente. Le alterazioni di altezza da realizzare con la trazione laterale della corda (bending) interessano le note comprese sotto al segno: ⌐ ¬. Se siete incerti sull'entità dell'innalzamento di tono da raggiungere, suonate le note indicate tastando normalmente la corda. Gli esempi seguenti mostrano le tecniche più comunemente impiegate nella maggior parte dei casi che possono presentarsi.

Esempio 1
Suonate il Re e innalzate di un tono (due mezzi toni) a Mi.

Esempio 2
Suonate il Re, tirate alzando di un tono a Mi e rilasciate tornando a Re. Va suonata solo la prima nota.

Esempio 3
'Bend Veloce': suonate il Re e quindi alzate di un tono a Mi il più velocemente possibile.

Esempio 4
'Pre-Bend': tastate il Re, tirate alzando di un tono a Mi e poi suonate.

Esempio 5
Suonate simultaneamente La e Si quindi tirate la 2a corda per innalzare il suono a Si.

Esempio 6
Suonate simultaneamente Re e Fa♯ quindi tirate la 3a corda alzando il suono di un tono a Mi, e la 2a corda di mezzo tono, alzando il suono a Sol.

Negli esempi seguenti sono illustrate altre tecniche chitarristiche:

Barra del tremolo
Alterate l'altezza del suono mediante la barra del tremolo. Dove possibile l'altezza da raggiungere è indicata.
a) Suonate il Sol e abbassate il suono fino a Mi mediante la barra.
b) Suonate il Sol a vuoto e scendete quanto più possibile.

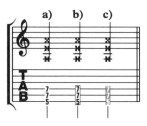

Smorzato
a) Smorzato con la destra
Smorzare le corde con il palmo della mano destra in prossimità del ponticello.
b) Smorzato con la sinistra
Smorzare le corde allentando la pressione delle dita subito dopo aver prodotto i suoni.
c) Pizzicato
Premere leggermente le corde in modo che non producano note ma soltanto un effetto percussivo.

Legature ascendenti e discendenti
Suonate la prima nota e ricavate la seconda percuotendo la corda con il dito contro la barretta; per la terza nota tirate la corda con il medesimo dito. Soltanto la prima nota va suonata.

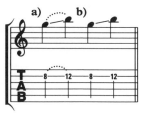

Glissando
a) Suonate la prima nota e ricavare la seconda facendo scivolare il dito lungo la corda. Va pizzicata solo la prima nota.
b) Come sopra, ma pizzicando anche la seconda nota.

Armonici naturali

Toccate leggermente la corda sulla barretta indicata e pizzicate col plettro per produrre un suono di campana. Le notine indicano il suono risultante, dove occorra.

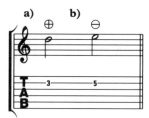

Slide Chitarra

a) Suonare con slide.
b) Suonare senza slide.

Armonici artificiali

Tastate la nota più bassa, toccate leggermente la corda sulla barretta relativa alla nota romboidale e pizzicate con il plettro. Le notine indicano il suono risultante.

Vibrato

Effettuate il vibrato facendo oscillare il dito che preme la corda oppure con la barra del tremolo. Poichè il vibrato è un fatto di gusto personale, viene indicato solo dove è essenziale.

Armonici pizzicati

Tastate normalmente la nota ma pizzicate la corda con la mano destra per ricavare l'armonico sopracuto. Le notine indicano l'altezza del suono risultante.

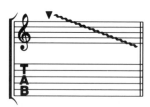

Suono graffiato

Fate scorrere il bordo del plettro lungo la corda. L'effetto è maggiore sulle corde fasciate.

Microintervalli

Una freccia diretta verso il basso significa che il suono scritto va abbassato di un intervallo inferiore al semitono; una freccia diretta verso l'alto innalza il suono scritto.

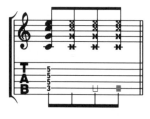

Accordi ripetuti

Per facilitare la lettura, possono venire omessi i numeri nell'intavolatura di un accordo ripetuto. L'esempio mostra un accordi di Do maggiore suonato normalmente, smorzato con la destra, smorzato con la sinistra e pizzicato (muto).

Accordature Speciali

Le accordature diverse da quella normale sono indicate in speciali 'gabbie di accordatura'. Ogni gabbia rappresenta una corda di chitarra; all'estremità sinistra corrisponde la corda più bassa. Il simbolo '•' in una gabbia sta ad indicare l'intonazione della corda corrispondente è quella normale. Una nota nella gabbia indica che l'intonazione di quella corda va modificata portandola all'altezza indicata. Per coloro che leggono l'intavolatura, dei numeri posti nelle gabbie stanno ad indicare di quanti semitoni deve salire o scendere l'intonazione della corda. L'intavolatura è da considerarsi relativa ad uno strumento accordato come indicato nelle gabbie.

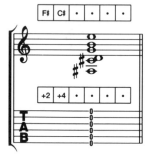

Accordate la corda del Mi basso (6a) un tono sopra (due semitoni) a Fa♯. Accordate la corda del La basso (5a) due toni sopra (quatro semitoni) a Do♯.

Indicazione degli accordi

E' stata impiegata la seguente nomenclatura convenzionale degli accordi.

Quando non compare la griglia appropriata di un accordo, ad esempio, quando la musica consiste nella ripetizione di una stessa figura (riff), la base tonale è indicata fra parentesi: **[C]**

Dove non è stato possibile trascivere il passaggio, compare il segno ∿ .

Printed in England
The Panda Group · Haverhill · Suffolk · 9/97